Yoga Bliss

Also by Sharon Heller, PhD

The Vital Touch -- How Intimate Contact with Your Baby Leads to Happier, Healthier Development (NY: Owl/Holt, 1997).

The Idiot's Guide to Conquering Fear and Anxiety (NY: Macmillan, 1999).

Too Loud, Too Bright, Too Fast, Too Tight: What to do if you are sensory defensive in an overstimulating world (NY: HarperCollins, December, 2002).

Uptight & Off Center, How Sensory Processing Disorder Throws Adults off Balance & How to Create Stability (Symmetry, 2015).

Anxiety: Hidden Causes, Why your anxiety may not be "all in your head but from something physical (Symmetry, 2010).

Yoga Bliss

How Sensory Input in Yoga Calms and Organizes the Nervous System

SHARON HELLER, PhD

SYMMETRY

Symmetry
Delray Beach, FL

Book cover by Sharon Heller (anya-heller.pixels.com)
Printed in the United States of America
1st printing – July, 2021
www.sharonheller.net

"Nothing is as important as an idea whose time has come."

~Victor Hugo

To all my extraordinary yoga teachers—
James, Judy, Philip, Frankie and Stephanie.

Acknowledgements

Heartfelt thanks to the many people who shared their stories with me. Special thanks to Judy Weaver, yoga teacher, yoga therapist extraordinaire, and founder and director of education of Connected Warriors in South Florida, who carefully read through the manuscript and provided valuable feedback. Much thanks to Heidi Rocke. The quintessential Renaissance lady, Heidi is another extraordinary yoga teacher and yoga therapist, an acupuncturist, and a superb writer and editor who provided the line editing. Last but not least, thank you to the forever youthful yogi Jen Dillard for taking the time to shoot most of the photos throughout the book.

Photo Models

Jen Dillard

James Kiger

Marjorie Hacker

Judy Weaver

Sharon Heller

Elizabeth Scheer

Ryan Perma

Gerry Gipson

Stephanie Dodge

Marissa Carrera

Alexis King

Anna Maria Aste

Daja Cook

Contents

Contents at a Glance

Sensory Integration: How Brain Organizes & Integrates Sensation
Well Organized Nervous System
Compromised Nervous System (Sensory Processing Disorder):
 Sensory Defensiveness (Hypersensitivity to Sensation)
 Hyposensitivity to Sensation
 Clumsiness
 Problems with Sensory Discrimination
 Auditory & Visual Processing Problems
How Compromised Nervous System Manifests in Yoga Practice

How Yoga Asanas Stimulate & Integrate Senses:
 Proprioceptive Input
 Vestibular Input
 Deep Pressure Touch
 Visual Input
 Auditory Input
How Yoga Employs Sensory Integration Principles:
 Muscle Development & Movement
 Bandhas
 Muscle Control & Balance
 Muscles & Body Awareness
 Body Awareness & Internal Sensation
  Hyposensitive
  Hypersensitive
 Motor Planning & Coordination
 Bilateral Coordination

Different Styles, Different Pranayama
  Ashtanga & Vinyasa
  Bikram
  Kundalini
  Anuttara Raja
    Alternate Nostril Breathing
  Vagus Nerve
  Heart Rate Variability (Hrv)
  Healthy Vagal Tone
  Boosting Vagal Tone
    Pranayama Breathing
    Humming & Chanting
    Smiling

Pranayama & Oxytocin

Yoga Encourages Mindfulness
Yoga Uses Both Top-Down Vs Bottom-Up Processing
In Yoga, Right, Creative, Intuitive Brain Takes Over
Yoga Gets You In Touch With Feelings by Encouraging:
  Conscious Awareness of Feelings & Intention
  Higher State of Consciousness
  Emotional Release
  Release of Trapped Emotions

Yoga Encourages Rewiring Brain (Neuroplasticity)
Yoga Increases Time Brain-Derived Neurotrophic Factor (BDNF)

Yoga Keeps You Present to Alleviate Depression
Yoga Enhances Social Bonding
Why We Feel Connected During Yoga:
  Release of:

Yoga Practice, Trains, & Improves:
Vestibular Functioning from All Head Changes
Proprioception from All Push & Pull
Visual Input through Focus & Dristi

Ways to Enhance Balance in Yoga Practice:
Remove Support
Vary Surface
Hang Like a Bat
Yoga Inversion Sling
Yoga Hanging Wall
Yoga Headstand Bench
Remove or Change Vision
Close Eyes
Change Head Position
Visualize
Buy Better Mat

How to Enhance Body Awareness in Yoga Practice:
Blocks
Sandbags
Strap
Balls
Eye Pillow
Hammock

How to Enhance Tactile Sensation in Yoga Practice:
Use Greater Force
Use Walls
Use Ropes
Do Partner Yoga
Fly Through Air
Use Yoga Mudras
Add Texture
Clothing
Mat
Mat Cover

How to Enhance Auditory Sensation in Yoga Practice:
Enhance Auditory Sensation
> *Voice Quality*
> *Music Choice Music Preference Timing*
> *Use Wordless Music*
> *Chant*
> *Vibrations*
> *Avoid No Music*

Scent in Yoga Practice

12. Sensory Rich Yoga Environment 293

Visual

> *Color*
> > *Avoid Eyestrain*
> > *Create Space & Warmth*
> > *Emotional Impact*
> > > *Green*
> > > *Blue*
> > > *Pink*

> *Walls*
> > *Mirrors*
> > > *Advantage*
> > > > *Act as Visual/Spatial Aid*
> > > *Disadvantages*
> > > > *Eliminates Use of That Wall*
> > > > *Interferes with Body Sensing*

> *Lighting*
> > *Natural Light with Muted Sunlight Works Best*
> > *Avoid Bright Spots*
> > *Avoid Fluorescent Lights Which Create Stress*
> > > *Reduce Heart Rate Variability (Vagal Tone)*
> > > *Raise Blood Pressure & Cortisol Level*
> > > *Noisy & Buzz*
> > > *Flicker*

INTRODUCTION

"The easiest step toward improving the quality of life consists in simply learning to control the body and its senses."

~Mihaly Csikszentmihali, Flow:
The Psychology of Optimal Experience

The arduous hour and a half Power Vinyasa class is at an end. Lying on my back in Savasana (the corpse pose)—eyes closed and eyeballs fallen into the orbits, arms spread and legs open slightly wider than the hips, palms up and chin slightly pulled down—my body, heavy, melts into the floor. My breathing slows to 3 to 4 times per minute and a quiet peace resides in my center.

I am lost in the moment. Time stands still and my mind floats above the clouds. The experience is the closest I come to a religious encounter.

All the strenuous effort of the last hour and a half has been a preparation for this serene, meditative place. I never want to leave.

Ahhh. Yoga bliss.

Typical for me is this quiet stillness and serenity at the end of Power Vinyasa Yoga: a vigorous, challenging Vinyasa-style practice consisting of a flowing, vigorous, dynamic sequence of poses, coordinated with breath.

This serenity took years to achieve.

On a warm, spring day in 1987, my life changed irrevocably. Exhausted after a day of teaching preschoolers in inner city Chicago, followed by a night of teaching college students at a community college, I tripped on my clogs and lunged headlong down a flight of concrete stairs. I crashed onto the right side of my head and suffered head trauma.

At first, the only apparent injuries were bruises, a cut above my right eye and a headache that subsided by the end of the week. "Okay," I thought. The worst that happened was stitches above my right eye and a black eye.

How wrong I was. The fall compressed and misaligned my skull and threw my whole body out of whack. Over the course of a year, neurological symptoms erupted and hijacked my life: my head felt as if wrapped in a vice and filled with cobwebs; my chest felt constricted and my jaw was clamped and painful from TMJ; my eyes were strained, darting and unfocused and my movements wavered.

Every noise, bright light, and strong odor attacked me. Touch created, in the words of Shakespeare, the "thousand natural shocks the flesh is heir to." Maneuvering through the world was like maneuvering through a sensory minefield: my life an on-going fire alarm—a condition called *sensory defensiveness* (see chapter one).

I was too bent out of shape to experience yoga bliss. As I describe in my book, *Too Loud, too Bright, too Fast, too Tight* ("she" being me),

"During class, the overhead lights, the whirring of the air conditioner, the rough carpet touching her feet, the body odors of others in the group, and her instructor's squeaky voice would grate on her nerves, even when she was not unduly stressed. During meditation, noises slit open her inner sanctum. Moreover, whatever relaxation these activities afforded seemed short lived."

Even during Savasana I couldn't unwind as my body was too wired, while my head burst with worried thoughts.

What was going on? I didn't know because I didn't connect my symptoms with having fallen down the flight of stairs.

In my 50's, I needed glasses for reading. The optometrist couldn't find the correct prescription. All that he prescribed created immediate eyestrain, as did putting on, even for a second all Sunglasses.

In 2000, I went to see Walter Chao, a developmental optometrist to see if he could figure out what was going on. He was miffed. "Your eyes behave like someone with traumatic brain injury," he told me.

What? How could that be?

In 2010, his diagnosis was confirmed by Dr. Craig McKeown at Bascom Palmer Eye Hospital in Miami. Dr. McKeown sent me to Nova University for eye vision therapy. It didn't help. Only this year did I discover the reason for my unusual vision problems and why no therapy could help: my right retina had been damaged during the fall.

In the meantime, when Dr. Chao first mentioned traumatic brain injury, I thought about the accident. When I told him about landing on my head, he said, "Ah. The problem with your vision might reside in your skull."

He suggested I see Lewis Arrandt, a chiropractor in Miami who performs neurocranial restructuring (NCR). An invasive cranial therapy, NCR involves inflating a balloon against the sphenoid bone, a linchpin in the cranium that articulates with all the other cranial bones. NCR focuses on precise realignment of the sphenoid to release connective tissues of the skull. As the head becomes symmetrical, tension patterns relax and the body's reflexes push the head straighter on the spine. This gradually optimizes the functions of the nervous system, spine and posture.

I made an appointment that day.

After examining me, Arrandt informed me that the fall had crunched my skull and spine. This created scoliosis (curved spine) and weakness on my right side where the muscles had atrophied and weakened, throwing my whole body out of whack.

"You've had no life," said Arrandt.

Someone understood!

I began therapy that day.

Changes happened, but very slowly.

I was a mess. Along with all the neurological symptoms, I was exhausted and I barely functioned. I had been a high energy, productive person before the fall. On a typical day, I taught young children until 3:00pm, then took a jazz dance class, went to the gym or attended class for my doctorate in developmental psychology, and studied for the rest of the evening. Now, by 6:00pm, all energy was spent and for the rest of the evening I did as little as possible to conserve what energy was left. The laundry piled up; dishes stacked in the sink; dust covered floor and furniture.

Drained and severely stressed from intense head pressure and spaciness, from unsteadiness and severe eye strain, from debilitating sensory defensiveness and malnourishment from extreme digestive issues, compounded with money problems as earning a living was a challenge in my incapacitated state I reached adrenal exhaustion.

The last stage of the stress response, adrenal exhaustion is a state of debilitating overload. The body becomes overworked and depleted of its normal energy reserves, and fatigue becomes chronic. Cortisol, the stress hormone remains high and you overreact or become unglued at the slightest stress.

I felt at once wired and spent. My head exploded, my heart pounded. My chest weighed a ton of bricks, my limbs were on fire. My feet and arms tingled, my body dragged. Self-calming was impossible.

Should I ignore what was going on in my body and push myself, I hit a brick wall and collapsed. The thought of putting a stamp on an envelope took me over the edge. I had gone from flight/fight to freeze, the state where animals play dead.

I could do ...nothing. Like a zombie, I crumbled onto my bed and lay still, on my back, in quiet darkness. In an hour or two, the debilitating state subsided enough for me to arise slowly and drag myself to do the bare minimum to survive. Writing, yoga, cooking, chatting on the phone—all were unthinkable. For years, I never washed my face or brushed my teeth before bed.

"OMG! How am I going to write *Too Loud, too Bright*," I worried as I was under contract with HarperCollins to do so. *"I'm going to have to return my advance!"*

And I didn't just worry about how to write the book. I worried about getting fired from teaching and how I would make a living.

At that time, I had a heavy teaching load as an adjunct professor of psychology and education courses at colleges and universities in South Florida.

I taught the classes in a twilight zone.

Though I had taught the same courses for several years, the class lecture would take hours to prepare, and I would fumble with the presentation. Unable to think on my feet, I would read from jumbled notes that threw me; "ums" punctuated my presentation. In front of me, I saw a muddled mass of students, unable to discern one face from the other, further throwing me. "Unavailable," "Out of it," read my student evaluations.

At the end of the last class of the term, I sat frozen in my seat, my brain too muddled and my body too exhausted to rise, remove the video tape from the VCR, and turn off the TV *without falling apart*. That was the last class I taught. To earn a living I turned to ghostwriting, as writing afforded me time to gather my thoughts and, when I crashed, to collapse into bed.

Weak, dizzy, depleted and unsteady, yoga felt like a torture chamber as I struggled through the asanas. Still, the mat afforded me a reprieve from otherwise unrelenting stress and I dragged myself to class.

Over time, with many sessions of NCR for the head trauma, a "sensory diet" to alleviate sensory defensiveness (explained in chapter two), and alternative healing modalities to calm and relax, detox and rejuvenate, and, of course, with taking yoga classes my nervous system settled.

I haven't and likely will never achieve neurological integrity. My normal is *mild* head pressure, *mild* eyestrain, *mild* light-headedness, mild hypersensitivity. And so it takes a bit of time for me to unwind on the mat.

But I do. Like clockwork, after 40 minutes or so into a Power Vinyasa yoga class—about the time we lean over and stretch into Triangle—I spontaneously inhale a slow, deep breath and feel at once lighter but grounded, as a warm buzz trickles through me. Stress washes out of my body like a spring rain. A load lifts from my shoulders and throughout the rest of the class, my body flows rhythmically through the poses like a sun drenched float down a lazy river.

By the end of class, mind, body and soul emit one elongated "Ooommmm."

"Yoga is invigoration in relaxation. Freedom in routine.
Confidence through self-control.
Energy within and energy without."

~YMBER DELECTO

What creates yoga bliss?

To many yogis, the answer is spiritual awakening, as described in yoga teachings.

Neuroscience offers a different explanation. It's about biochemistry.

In yoga, you move through a series of poses (asanas) that involve considerable proprioceptive input (sense of body awareness from input into the joints and muscles), vestibular input (sense of balance from moving in a different plane) and tactile input from deep pressure applied to your body against floor or wall.

These three "primary" senses are our power senses. Strong input into these three, bolstered by deep breathing throughout the practice is the secret behind yoga bliss.

"Primary senses?" You might be shaking your head. Don't we have only five senses: touch, vision, hearing, smell, taste? No. These five senses are only what most people are aware of. In truth we have at least seven senses, including the vestibular and proprioceptive.

Our "far" senses—seeing, hearing, smelling, tasting and touching—inform us of what is happening outside our bodies and are supporting players in our sensory repertoire.

Our "near" senses, the vestibular and proprioceptive (experienced when we move) and the tactile (being touched) are our internal senses, informing us of what is happening inside our bodies. The main players in our sensory repertoire, they give the nervous system the most power.

Consider this. We can cover our ears, close our eyes, hold our nose, and close our mouth and function, as we do if deaf or blind. But turn off sensation into our skin as when we're paralyzed and we lose independence and, for some will to live. Turn off the sense of our body in space, or the sense of our body against gravity and we'd float into the space like astronauts.

If you aren't quite grasping the essential importance of these primary senses, think of yoga bliss as womb comfort, as that "oceanic feeling," as Sigmund Freud called it.

Inside the womb, the fetus is tightly contained, joints bent into a fetal tuck (somatosensory—tactile/proprioceptive input) and squeezed within wet warmth (tactile input). The newly forming body is constantly swayed and jolted (vestibular/proprioceptive input) as the mother moves, and experiences rhythmical movement as the mother walks (vestibular input). Once born, the baby on the mother's body continues to receive this rich sensory input. With it, the baby experiences a "Womb with a view," as social scientist Ashley Montagu quipped, and explored in detail in my book, *The Vital Touch*.

Seeking womb comfort is a lifelong quest. Embodying organizing sensations into everyday life is our best road to that lost paradise. And few activities offer this more than yoga does.

During yoga practice, strong sensory input from the three primary senses releases at once a calming, visceral, and energizing chemical cocktail.

For a huge dose of happiness, you get a release of the four happiness hormones: Dopamine, our reward neurotransmitter; Oxytocin, our "love" hormone; Serotonin, our feel good neurotransmitter; Endorphins, the brain's opium. These hormones relax you by lowering cortisol, by increasing oxygen consumption, and by reducing muscle stiffness and tension.

For a huge dose of energy and mild stimulation, you get a release of invigorating adrenaline and norepinephrine-type stimulating compounds. This release happens especially after a strong vestibular hit from difficult inversions, like a headstand, where energy pulses through your limbs, and you feel so alive.

Think of the practice as a powerful pharmacy within your system. For happiness and youthful vitality, your prescription pad should read: one hour or more of yoga daily for a strong dose of vestibular, proprioceptive and tactile input.

Given this "medicine," researcher Catherine Woodyard reveals what you might have to look forward to. Exploring the therapeutic effects of yoga, Woodyard found yogic practices enhanced muscular strength and body flexibility; promoted and improved respiratory and cardiovascular function; promoted recovery from and treatment of addiction; reduced stress, anxiety, depression, and chronic pain; improved sleep patterns; and enhanced overall well-being and quality of life.

What pill can do that? What pill changes brain waves?

Brain Waves

Accompanying the above described chemical cascade is a change in brain waves, electrical flows that pass between the cranial nerves. As you move through asanas, mid-range beta brain waves (15HZ to 18HZ), our fast brain waves present during waking and driven by dopamine, give you the mental focus and alertness needed for movement.

These fast brain waves combine with the slower, relaxing, alpha brain waves (8Hz to 12Hz), the state between awake and asleep.

DIGGING DEEPER

"The beta brain-wave state is like a busy city with its excitement and vitality, but the alpha brain-wave state is like being in a beautiful countryside with the constant physical sensations of the sound of birds singing and water bubbling in a stream, the sight of every shade of green imaginable...." (p. 161). So writes Patt Lind-Kyle in *Heal Your Mind Rewire Your Brain*.

Needed for sensory perception, alpha brain waves enable us to pay attention to certain sensations and ignore others. When you focus on shifting your body in Warrior III to staying balanced on one leg while tuning out the horn honking outside, your brain is alight with alpha waves.

The result of the combined beta and alpha brain waves is feeling both energized and calm. If this doesn't happen and you remain wired during practice, as happened to me following my fall, blame it on an excess of very fast beta waves (18+ HZ), drowning out the slower alpha waves. If you remain sluggish during practice, beta brain wave activity is too low (12-15 HZ).

During meditation at the end of class, alpha combines with the slower, meditative theta brain waves (4Hz to 7Hz), the brain waves we experience in the state of sleep, dreams and REM (Rapid Eye Movement). You know theta waves are present when all thought ceases, you're barely aware of your body and the last time you took a breath, and a sublime peace descends upon you.

To awaken out of this euphoria and back to reality, the teacher will say, "*Slowly* return your body by wiggling fingers and toes. *Slowly* stretch arms and legs. *Slowly* turn your body to the right. *Slowly* make your way to Easy Pose."

In Easy Pose, you sit, eyes closed, still deep under.

(James)

Only after inspiring words from the teacher and "Namaste" (Hindu for 'I bow to the divine in you') do you open your eyes and slowly move your body to shift brain waves from alpha to beta, awakening you. Now alert, you roll up your mat, give sisterly hugs, laugh, and chatter in a love fest as, blissed-out, you saunter out the door.

Scientific studies support changes in brain waves during yoga practice. One study published in 2015 in *Complementary Therapies in Clinical Practice* by Desai and colleagues examined and reviewed fifteen articles on the effects of yoga on brain waves and structural changes and activation. It concluded that breathing, meditation, and posture-based yoga increased overall brain wave activity.

Not all yoga classes have an equal blissed out impact. Depending on the extent and intensity of these primary power senses during practice, bliss will fluctuate from settled, tranquil, and content to alive, exhilarated, and euphoric.

In more strenuous and athletic classes, like Power Vinyasa and Ashtanga, classes that require stamina, flexibility, and mastery of your body, strong proprioceptive and vestibular sensation interweave throughout the practice. This happens especially from challenging inversions and balancing postures— my Vinyasa class is like Cirque de Soleil!—deepening and extending bliss.

The "real" yogis who take these classes, those nimble, slender wonders with pronounced biceps, deep breathing, long lunges, elongated stretches, silent floating and arching back bends tend to hit the mat daily, living and breathing this energizing, serene, ancient Eastern practice. Imagine how good life must feel inside *their* bodies.

> *"Most people have no idea how good their body is designed to feel."*
>
> ~KEVIN TRUDEAU

As a senior with a slew of physical problems, including lordosis of spine and neck, scoliosis and fused vertebrae, I taper my practice and, though having practiced for 25 years, I consider myself intermediate: I step, not leap from Downward-Facing Dog to Forward Bend; I slide from Plank to Upward-Facing-Dog, skipping the Chaturanga (a push-up) between the two poses; I squat, place my hands on the floor and lean forward in Crow, omitting the lifting of feet to balance on arms.

And so I don't experience the deep euphoria that perhaps the hipless, slim, firm diehard yogi millennials populating my Power Vinyasa yoga class do.

I know the feeling, though, from my dance days. One time, while rehearsing "Michaelangelo: A Portrait in Dance" for PBS that I performed with Gus Giordano's company at age 22, I reached such an extraordinary high that I felt if I lifted my arms I might fly up in the air.

(Sharon, bottom left)

Still, Vinyasa gets me to a great place and, addicted to the high, I'm usually on the mat six to seven days a week.

Nor do you have to be a diehard yogi to benefit from yoga's power. Even in a slow-paced hatha yoga class, consisting largely of gentle stretches and breathing exercises and popular with beginners, or chair yoga, popular with seniors and the injured most report feeling calmer and less stressed.

Is it any wonder an estimated 35 million people practice yoga in the United States alone? According to national survey data from 2012, 94% of adult yogis do so for wellness related reasons: 86% said it reduced stress; 67% said it helped them feel better emotionally; 63% said it motivated them to exercise more regularly; 59% said it improved sleep.

"Yoga is a metaphor for life. You have to take it really slowly. You can't rush. You can't skip the next position. You find yourself in very humiliating situations, but you can't judge yourself. You just have to breathe, and let go."

~MADONNA

Yoga is an antidote to the ravages of our sedentary, unnaturally slumped lifestyle. Rather than hunched over a desk, we're standing upright in Mountain. Rather than staring at a screen, we're staring at a spot on the wall (dristi) to help us balance in Tree. Rather than wearing shoes which can deform and squish toes, ruin posture and cause problems like corns and bunions, shin splints and plantar fasciitis, we're barefoot on the mat. Rather than filling our heads with constant worry, we're present in the moment.

Perhaps yoga's worldwide popularity is an ancient evolutionary call to return to our essence.

The body was designed to move. Our early ancestors hunted and foraged for food and water, carried children, and hauled tubers and melons. Hard work and much walking and running were adaptive for survival and kept bodies and minds working well. The day ended with tranquility and sleep.

As little as 75 years ago, before modern technology made us sedentary, movement was woven into everyday life: we strolled to the store and sprinted to catch the bus; we carried groceries home and trekked up and down stairs, some with a baby in arms. Kids played outside, walked and biked to school, roller skated to the store, planted a garden, pushed a lawnmower and shoveled snow. Farm folks milked cows, rode horses, pitched hay, cleaned out the barn, and carried water from the well.

What has happened to our bodies in modern, technological life is a tragedy: we were never designed to be couch/mouse potatoes. Consider for instance, the perils of sitting in a chair. In addition to not moving our bodies, sitting all day on our derriere results in loss of flexibility and awareness in our spine. Without a flexible spine, we can't have a flexible body. The fleshy, slouched, awkward and painful bodies so many modern folks inhabit reflect such an anti-biological sedentary lifestyle.

"Take care of your body, it's the only place you have to live."

~JIM ROHN

Through the forward bends, backward bends, sideward bends, twists and inversions in a yoga practice, our bodies move the ways they were built to move. In fact, a fundamental aspect of yoga practice is the awakening of the spine to undulate backwards and forwards, undulate side-to-side, and to twist. Such awakening straightens out the spine to enable one to sit upright longer in meditation—the true purpose of yoga.

The first time the writer Elizabeth Gilbert, author of the bestseller *Eat, Pray, Love* arrived in yoga class, she thought it too New Agey. "First of all, there was that solemn smell of incense, which seemed excessively serious and sort of ridiculous to somebody who was far more accustomed to the smells of cigarettes and beer," she said in a 2017 interview with *Yoga Journal.* "Then there was the music. (Chanting, heaven help us!)....And the teacher...started prattling on about how the sound of Om was the primordial cause of the universe, and so on."

Bored and uncomfortable, she wanted to flee the class—until they did a side twist. And then revelation: "I knew without any doubt that my spine had never made this simple but precise shape before—this twist, this reach, this profound extension. Something shifted. Something lifted...my spine started speaking to me, almost crying out to me. My spine said something like, "Oh my God, oh my dear sweet heavenly mercy—please don't stop, for this is what I have always needed, and this is what I will need every day for the rest of my life, finally, finally, finally..."

With a healthy, flexible spine, bodies stay fit: postures erect; shoulders retracted; bones strong.

"You're as young as your spine is flexible."

~JOSEPH PILATES

In my twilight years, my spine remains flexible. I stand tall at 5'3"—the same height I was at 17—and peer down at many of my hunched contemporaries as their stiff, slumped bodies shrink into the ground.

One of my most memorable and life changing moments came a few years ago when, out of nowhere, Gerry, one of my yoga teachers sauntered up to me, gave me a hug, and said, "I love your yoga body."

Wow! In my 70's I still had a yoga body—upright, solid, firm and toned. From that day on, whenever I felt not up to going to class, or wanted to binge on a pint of mocha almond coconut ice cream, Gerry's words would ring in my ears and I would think, "Nope. I can't lose my yoga body."

Vanity made me feel that way. What I didn't realize was that having a yoga body also makes me happier. Research has found that by standing up straight our attitude changes. We feel more enthusiastic and less discouraged; more courageous and less fearful; calmer and less jumpy; alert and less sluggish just by getting us to stand and sit straighter: "Up!" is the magic word in yoga.

Other strenuous exercise, like aerobics bathes the nervous system with power sensations, calming and relaxing us, but doesn't have the same effect on posture. Moreover, research confirms greater emotional stability and well-being from yoga practice than other type of exercise. "I Do Yoga to Burn Off the Crazy," touts a yoga T-shirt so popular it's sold in the mega giant Walmart.

How well does *your* nervous system function?

This book will answer that question and more. Here's a sample of what you will learn.

If you are yogi or wish to become on, you will learn how sensory input:

- Enhances body awareness and feeling grounded;

- Increases balance, for senior citizens especially;

- Reduces stress, agitation, or tension by shifting the autonomic nervous system from sympathetic arousal flight-fight mode to parasympathetic, calming and organizing mode;

- Alleviates mental health issues like anxiety, depression, PTSD, panic and dissociation that has not responded effectively to psychotropic drugs or therapy as research documents yoga to be superior to other forms of exercise in positively affecting mood and anxiety.

If you are a yoga teacher or wish to become one, you will learn:

- How sensory processing affects yoga practice: reducing stress; increasing body awareness; building balance; and enhancing self-regulation, focus, concentration and even memory;

- How different sensory needs of students, including those who are hyper-responsive to sensation and those with hypotonia (low muscle tone) affect yoga practice;

- Ways sensory processing can enhance practice, including:
  - Using props like the wall, blocks and the strap to increase proprioception and deep pressure;
  - Enhancing vestibular input by challenging balance (closing eyes while trying to balance; standing on uneven surface);
  - Choosing the best music.

- Effect of lighting, colors, flooring, ceiling height, temperature, flooring, windows and so forth on wellbeing during yoga class.

How to Use this Book

Yoga Bliss is designed for anyone who practices or teaches yoga and wants a better understanding of why yoga makes you feel so good. To meet this goal, the book contains much information on the sensory input of the practice and on neuroscience.

If you're just starting out or want to begin a practice there's lots of useful information on the different styles of yoga and what the different classes consist of. If you're a seasoned yogi, you can skim these parts and concentrate on the science of yoga bliss.

Yoga Bliss consists of three parts and twelve chapters.

Part I, *The Senses*, consists of seven chapters explaining sensory processing.

Chapter one introduces the theory of sensory integration, a paradigm new to most that sets the tone for understanding yoga bliss.

Chapter two discusses the different aspects of sensory integration and how yoga incorporates them.

Chapter three discusses sensory modulation, the ability to maintain a steady state so you're neither bored nor over-stimulated.

Chapter four discusses the vestibular/balance sense, its impact on functioning and role in yoga practice.

Chapter five discusses the proprioceptive/body awareness sense, its impact on functioning and role in yoga practice.

Chapter six discusses the tactile sense, its impact on functioning and role in yoga practice.

Chapter seven talks about Pranayama or yoga breathing, a practice central to yoga, and to yoga's ability to calm the nervous system.

Part II, *The Science*, consists of two chapters that describe the neuroscience behind yoga bliss and its application to the healing process.

Chapter eight discusses the mind/body connection in yoga practice.

Chapter nine talks about yoga as therapy for conditions such as depression, sensory processing disorder, and PTSD.

Part III, *The Practice* describes the power of the poses and ways to enhance practice and environment.

Chapter ten goes through different asanas and the primary sensations experienced in the poses.

Chapter eleven looks at ways to enhance sensory input throughout practice.

Chapter twelve discusses ways to create a sensory rich yoga environment.

Join me now for a journey into the largely unexplored territory of the science behind yoga bliss.

PART I
THE SENSES

"Health is aliveness, spontaneity, gracefulness and rhythm."

~ Alexander Lowen, M.D.

CHAPTER 1

SENSORY HARMONY

"I could discover my body anew every day, and through it discover the world around me. I could start again – remake my universe."

~ELIZABETH KADETSKY, *FIRST THERE IS A MOUNTAIN*

When asked what he regretted most in life, Sigmund Freud, the founder of psychoanalysis and one of the most influential geniuses of the last century replied, ironically, "I wished I had been given a better brain."

My wish would be for a more organized nervous system. Who wouldn't wish that! The more balanced and organized the nervous system, the steadier we are: on our feet; in our moods; in our thinking; in our life.

All behavior relies on the organization of the nervous system. As the brilliantly insightful occupational therapist Patti Oetter, my mentor put it:

"Behavior is a reflection of the organization of the nervous system at that moment and under those conditions."

Those words, spoken to me over lunch one day in Los Angeles twenty years ago, widened the lens from which I viewed human behavior, a subject that, as a psychologist I know a bit about, and changed profoundly how I understand the impact of body on mind. I learned that how we interpret and respond to sensory information underlies all human behavior. Without knowing a person's sensory world, you can't understand their behavior.

Our thoughts, actions, and feelings and how we express them—our *behavior*—begins with how the brain codes and processes sensory information. If we feel bored, we seek sensation; if we feel overwhelmed, we avoid sensation. Both states drive us and divert our attention away from what's going on in the world. For this reason, behavior is not easily modified until sensory needs are met.

To understand why, let's explore the process called *sensory integration.*

SENSORY INTEGRATION

"To understand what it means to think, to compute information, to have a trillion neurons firing in my brain, to have consciousness either at a 40 Hz frequency (F. Crick) or at the quantum level (Penrose), one must really understand this: it's all about bodily sensation."

~CHARLES WOLF

How our brain integrates and makes sense of incoming sensory information relies on how well our brain processes sensory information.

Let me explain.

To move the body effectively and to think clearly, the brain must organize and integrate the bombardment of sensation impacting us at any point in time: sensation from one's own body—vestibular (sense of balance); proprioceptive (sense of body awareness); tactile (sense of touch); and sensation from the environment—sound, vision, smell, taste.

This process is called *sensory integration* (SI), the theory of which was first conceived in the 1970's by occupational therapist A. Jean Ayres. SI forms the basis for how we make sense of the world.

Sounds straight forward. It's not.

How well our brains interpret the sensory world varies, from those who see though a clear lens and glide through the world with ease, to those who see through a distorted lens and struggle with the slightest obstacle.

Well Organized Nervous System

If you have good sensory integration you make sense of what is seen, heard, smelled, and felt and respond appropriately and adaptively. You easily block out irrelevant stimuli, neither overly seeking nor overly avoiding sensation, control impulses and persist in tasks, navigate space with ease and move as a compact presence in the world.

As your brain appraises sensation appropriately, you are sound in body and mind, alert and adaptive, functioning well and thriving. You maintain a comfortable steady state and regular body rhythms for sleep, rising, eating, eliminating. At the same time, a steady state allows the higher, thinking brain to function optimally and you feel competent, capable, motivated and in charge of destiny.

My friend Josie, whom I've known since grammar school is an example of great sensory integration. Smart, funny, competent, outgoing, even-tempered, a good athlete with great posture (this has importance for nervous system integrity), and a good listener, she was one of the popular girls, admired by all. Steady and stable, independent and self-contained still today, never having shown, to my knowledge addictive behavior or neurotic musings, she has, throughout life, enjoyed warm and loving relationships, a satisfying career, many friends and much joy.

Unfortunately, few of us have that well-organized of a nervous system. Most of us have average SI. We may be a bit clumsy and uncoordinated; a bit distracted and spacey; a bit messy and disorganized; a bit reactive to noise and bright lights; a bit of a loner or a social nerd. In an article published in 2013 in *Journal of Neurodevelopmental Disorders*, one research team led by Nava Levit-Binnun found 17 studies that reported sensory and motor abnormalities in healthy individuals.

A bit off center, we get by—with a few glitches. We call these glitches stupidity, anxiety, stress, depression, laziness, and so on, and the world generally agrees with our assessment.

Consider a sampling of glitches during yoga practice that you believe or others have told you about yourself.

You don't extend your body as forcefully into an asana as do others because you're "lazy." In truth, it's because you have low muscle tone and it takes more effort than most (9 times more) to move your body.

You avoid eye contact with the teacher because you're "rude." In truth, eye contact, to you, is overstimulating.

You fail to follow the teacher's instructions to "spread your palms, index fingers parallel or slightly turned out, and turn your toes under" in Downward-Facing Dog because you're "stupid." In truth, you have slow auditory processing and your brain can't process that many instructions at once.

You flinch when the teacher adjusts you because you "don't like that teacher." In truth, her touch was light and light touch can register in your brain as "danger!"

You avoid the camel pose (an intense and often fear inspiring backbend) because you're "afraid to face your fears." In truth, your balance (vestibular) system is off and your brain triggers "I'm falling" when you bend your head all the way back, behind the center of gravity.

You move your mat too close to others because you are "inconsiderate of the other's space." In truth, you seek closeness because you crave touch to modulate your nervous system.

For some of you reading this, such incidents ring a bell.

How have you coped with your limitations? You compensated. Said Patti Oetter: "The majority of us have escaped diagnosis but know our limitations well. We have learned strategies to capitalize on our strengths and cover or avoid those things most difficult."

Born Uptight & Off Center

Initially, I fell into this "escaped diagnosis" category.

All my life, I've had slow auditory processing. To grasp the meaning of a movie, I needed to watch it twice or I missed out on much information. In school, I had difficulty following the teacher's verbal instructions and froze when asked a question. Likewise, when teaching college, my mind went blank when asked a question to which I didn't know the answer. Fortunately, I taught the same psychology classes for many years and this happened rarely. When it did, I compensated with the Talmudic trick of answering a question with a question.

I had visual-spatial deficits that created embarrassment. In 8th grade Home Ed, having cut out an apron, I was told to cut a pocket from leftover material. I cut out *the center of the apron*. I felt dumb. My family concurred and often laughed at stupid things I would do because my eyes weren't taking in the whole picture.

In my 30's, I was determined to make clothes to better suit my style than the current 80's fashion of tight pants, tight skirts, bold colors, sequins and leather. Again taking to the sewing machine, I created full, long, solid color dresses to reflect my serious, intellectual nature as a student at the University of Chicago. Invariably, I had to buy twice as much fabric as required because whatever I sewed was cut or stitched *at least twice*. Frustrating. But the joy of wearing *my* style of clothes compensated.

The worst, though, was how a poor visual-spatial map affected my dancing.

In my youth, I took dance classes, mostly jazz. In class, you learn a dance routine taught in orderly, short sequences. By the end of class, most of the students were joyfully dancing away, the steps learned and automatic.

Not me. In an act of betrayal, my brain failed to translate what the teacher's feet were doing into my feet; learning even a few steps in a sequence took great effort. Nervously, I paced, trying to figure out the steps. Needless to say, I never made it to Broadway.

Still, I persisted and, ignoring my weaknesses and capitalizing on the strength of having a gracefully flowing body, I became a good enough dancer to perform with Gus Giordano's dance company on PBS at age 22.

Likewise, I compensated for slow auditory and visual processing with strong verbal skills that enabled me to get first a bachelor's degree, then a master's degree in child development, and, in my early 40's, a PhD in developmental psychology, and to teach first kids and later college students, and publish four books.

Nor did my crazy eyes stop me from later becoming a painter (under the nom de artiste, "Anya Heller"). Though my paintings lack anatomical precision, reflecting my poor visual-spatial skills, they have vivid color and a dynamic composition of bold flowing lines to reveal rhythm and movement.

How did I make sense of all these shortcomings? I didn't. I either buried them or assumed I was an idiot, weird, or crazy. In eighth grade I signed my name in someone's autograph book, "Goofy." That was the state of my self-esteem. In spite of how well I compensated, something deep inside of me felt deficient and inept.

Finally, in the 50's, I discovered the true cause of my shortcomings: *sensory processing disorder.* Only then could I show self-compassion.

Not Making Sense of Things

Sensory processing disorder (SPD) is a relatively unknown condition in which sensory messages scramble in the brain. This causes a "traffic jam" on the sensory highway, blocking you from making sense of or responding appropriately to your world.

The result is a variety of symptoms likely to ring a bell for many: sensory defensiveness; hypersensitivity to sensation (jumping from sudden noise), or the opposite, hyposensitivity to sensation (not detecting the milk is sour); clumsiness and lack of coordination (two left feet); problems with sensory discrimination (unable to discern the sensation of a peach from a mango); auditory and visual processing problems (slow in making sense of what you hear and see).

Though relatively unknown, SPD is common, with estimates of those suffering it to some degree to be as high as 30% of the US population. Of that, 10% have sensory processing disorder severe enough to interfere with functioning and they stand out as off kilter and even odd. These are mainly special needs kids who don't adapt easily to school: some with learning disabilities; some with ADHD; some on the autistic spectrum.

Another 20%, or so, suffer it mildly, feeling uptight and off center but functioning. You know—half of your relatives, co-workers and friends!

From the Frying Pan to the Fire

Initially, I fell into that 20% "mild" range. And then, in 1987, after my fall down a flight of stairs, I plummeted into the 10%. In the opening of my book, *Too Loud, too Bright, too Fast, too Tight*, I describe my experience.

> *"Relax," people would tell Dr. H., a college professor, "stop letting everything bother you." But she couldn't and she didn't know why. The labels in her clothing, the sound of someone opening a bag of potato chips, the odor of her new car, the flashing pointer on the computer screen, the computer's hovering noise—everything seemed to drive her crazy."*

The severe defensiveness, auditory and visual processing problems, along with on-going head pressure, TMJ, severe eyestrain, weakness, and digestive issues rendered me barely functional. In a split second, I graduated from mild, *"I can cope and get by"* SPD, to moderate and at times extreme, *"I'm falling apart"* SPD. The result was a chaotic, moment to moment struggle to stay afloat.

Living with Chaos

On the moderate to extreme end of SPD, life is chaos. Messages scramble, over- or under filtered, confusing you; what might be simple and automatic to the normal brain becomes perplexing, irritating, effortful, even, at times, impossible—at times I felt like a stammering idiot. Spontaneous behavior like righting yourself when you start to fall takes conscious effort and energy, and, in spite of best efforts, your response is inefficient, excessive or useless and you fall.

Those who are hypersensitive to sensation like me have a low sensory threshold and get easily overwhelmed; the hum of the air conditioning, the tag in your shirt, the sun's rays, the smell of chlorine and a thousand other sensations can be maddening.

Those who are hyposensitive have a high sensory threshold and barely register sensation; sounds like a barking dog, or awareness of an ant crawling up your arm eludes you—think of those yogis lying on a bed of nails. My mother, with moderate SPD was like this. She was unable to smell rancid milk and got sick once from drinking spoiled milk. Nor did she see her world clearly, though her vision was fine. One day, she announced frantically that our cat was lying on our driveway not moving. I rushed out the door. It was a dead possum.

Peering inside her brain would have offered explanation.

Lack of alpha wave activity led to lack of awareness of sensation. Without awareness of sensation, you can become forgetful as sensation acts as information and is processed into memories and thoughts. My mother constantly lost her keys and missed appointments.

Too little alpha wave activity meant too slow mental speed to connect thoughts with sensations. And that makes it difficult to react to information quickly enough, explaining why my mother made little sense of her world.

It's hard to calm with low alpha wave activity. My mother was a nervous wreck, set off at the drop of a button. When I would get upset, she would scream, *"Don't get hysterical!"*

Whether hyper and overwhelmed by sensation, or hypo and missing out on sensation, you make little sense of things because both states leave you stuck in the primitive, survival brain and unable to think clearly. You might innocently say and do things at the wrong time, in the wrong place, and in the wrong way—I can't tell you how many times that happened to me!

Unstable, neurotic, crazed, you go to extremes to balance your nervous system and cope with stressors: if easily overexcited, you flee the feast and become withdrawn, as I did, and depressed; if easily bored, you focus on nothing else but the feast and, anxious and antsy, become easy prey to substance abuse and other addictions.

Desperate to escape the steep, treacherous path you traverse with missteps. You turn to doctors hoping for an elixir. Instead, you get misdiagnosed as anxious or depressed, as few physicians or therapists know about sensory processing disorder and, with little other than psychotropic drugs in their arsenal, dispense Xanax and Prozac like candy.

For some, the pills help to take the edge off. For others, they do nothing as SPD is neurological, not psychological. I tore up the prescription. I knew, intuitively something other than anxiety was going on. But what?

In 1991, while writing my first book, *The Vital Touch*, a book on babies and touch, I got my answer.

Meeting the Sensory Buddhas

In researching information for *The Vital Touch*, I came upon a talk by occupational therapist Patricia Wilbarger. In her talk Wilbarger described an extreme reaction to light touch in Dustin, an infant with whom she was working, a condition she called "tactile defensiveness."

Ha! That sounds like me. Whereas before I had loved to be touched and wore any texture clothing, sensory thorns now defined my life. I grimaced when someone tapped my shoulder, bristled when wearing wool, ripped out tags in my clothing, and shuddered when the sheets touched my skin when hitting my bed at night.

I called Wilbarger, a personable and passionate person. "Could adults suffer tactile defensiveness?" I asked. "Yep," she confirmed and it sure sounded like I did. Why don't I come to a workshop she and occupational therapist Patti Oetter were giving in the panhandle in Florida on sensory defensiveness?

I did and discovered the extraordinary and largely unknown field of sensory integration. I now knew not only the *why* for my angst but *what* to do for it: feed the nervous system the nourishing sensations it needs to become organized.

Armed with this information, my whole *weltanschauung* changed. I now not only saw my own behavior from a new, more encompassing perspective, but understood people with far greater depth than before discovering sensory integration.

As one of the first psychologists to embrace the idea of SI as the foundation of human behavior, I discovered how sensory issues create, mimic or exacerbate many mental health issues— from anxiety to anorexia to panic attack to depersonalization. In my books, *Too Loud, too Bright, too Fast, too Tight* and *Uptight and Off Center,* I discuss how alleviating sensory issues in your life alleviates anxiety and depression for many, leading to overall better mental health.

Off to See the Wizard

In 1998, I travelled to the Ayres clinic in Torrance, California for evaluation and SI therapy for two hours a day for five days with Patti Oetter. After evaluating me, Patti informed me that I had not only sensory defensiveness—in addition to touch, I was unable to tolerate noise, bright lights, or strong odors—but bilateral integration issues, visual-spatial processing issues, as well as slow auditory processing, all of which are part of sensory processing disorder. These issues, thought Patti, likely stemmed from birth trauma from the use of forceps, as well as from having had a concussion at age five when my mother found me unconscious on the doorstep.

Ahhh. What relief! Everything made sense. I wasn't dumb. I was smart with a few glitches that had obstructed my path to success.

Patti sent me home with a "sensory diet." For tactile defensiveness, she prescribed the Wilbarger therapressure protocol (a specific protocol of deep brushing of the skin followed by proprioceptive input); for auditory issues, a listening program (Sennheiser CDs); for visual-spatial issues, recommendation to see a developmental optometrist; for sensory modulation, a daily protocol of sensori-motor activities focused on intense "heavy work" (pushing and pulling against the body) and vestibular input.

To stay organized, I needed to feed my nervous system healing sensation at intervals throughout the day, as most sensori-motor interventions balance the nervous system for only an hour and a half to two hours. Following an intense yoga class, notice how long you remain balanced and organized.

To start my day, Patti told me to plod up and down stairs carrying a book bag for heavy work into the joints and muscles, and, early in the day, to swing on a swingset for around 15 minutes for vestibular input. The most powerful and longest lasting of all sensation, specific vestibular input like swinging impacts the system long after experiencing the stimulation. In treating special needs children, occupational therapists have found that fifteen minutes of swinging can have a 6-8 hour effect on the brain.

Other activities she recommended were: yoga, of course, dancing, biking (preferably uphill for more proprioception), a home trampoline, horseback riding, and walking in water.

Armed with this new paradigm, I felt galvanized to change my path to one less bumpy. I even arranged my day to include a trip to the park to swing on a swing with the kiddies. After a bit, I bought a home swing, a crocheted swing/chair attached to a doorway. Although, when that broke, I stopped swinging.

At that time, I was well into writing *Too Loud, too Bright* and, newly, sensory processing savvy. Yoga, with all its head changes was, I knew, replete with vestibular input. As I could balance in difficult poses like Tree or Warrior III, my balance didn't appear that bad. Could yoga be giving me the vestibular boost my system needed?

Indeed.

Yoga practice, when done often and consistently, with conviction and effort, converts brilliantly the nervous system to more organized, enhanced sensory integration. The result translates to more balanced behavior, and accounts for the thousands upon thousands of testimonials of people describing yoga as transforming their lives.

Let's explore the many ways yoga utilizes sensory processing to do so.

RECAP

SENSORY INTEGRATION: How the brain organizes and integrates the bombardment of sensation impacting us at any point in time:

- Sensation from one's own body:

- Vestibular (sense of balance);

- Proprioceptive (sense of body awareness);

- Tactile (sense of touch);

- Sensation from the environment: sound, vision, smell, taste.

WELL ORGANIZED NERVOUS SYSTEM:

- Make sense of what is seen, heard, smelled, and felt;

- Respond appropriately and adaptively;

- Easily block out irrelevant stimuli, neither overly seeking nor overly avoiding sensation;

- Control impulses;

- Persist in tasks;

- Navigate space with ease;

- Move as a compact presence in the world.

AVERAGE ORGANIZED NERVOUS SYSTEM:

- Bit clumsy and uncoordinated;

- Bit distracted and spacey;

- Bit messy and disorganized;

- Bit reactive to noise and bright lights;

POORLY ORGANIZED NERVOUS SYSTEM— SENSORY PROCESSING DISORDER: Relatively unknown condition in which sensory messages scramble in the brain and you don't make good sense of or responding appropriately to your world.

Symptoms:

- Sensory defensiveness: hypersensitivity to sensation (jumping from sudden noise, e.g.)

- Hyposensitivity to sensation (not detecting the milk is sour, e.g.);

- Clumsiness and lack of coordination (two left feet);

- Problems with sensory discrimination (unable to discern the sensation of a peach from a mango, e.g.);

- Auditory and visual processing problems (slow in making sense of what you hear and see).

Moderate to extreme end typified by:

- Chaos

- Confusion

- Easily frustrated

- Easily overwhelmed

- Make little sense of things

- Unstable, neurotic, crazed

How It Might Manifest in Yoga:

- Don't extend your body as forcefully into an asana from low muscle tone (takes 9 times more effort than most to move your body).

- Avoid eye contact with the teacher because eye contact is overstimulating.

- Fail to follow the teacher's instructions because you have slow auditory processing and your brain can't process that many instructions at once.

- Flinch when teacher adjusts you.

- Avoid camel pose because balance (vestibular) system is off.

- Move your mat too close to others because you crave touch to modulate your nervous system and seek closeness.

CHAPTER 2

YOGA AS SENSORY HAVEN

"When it comes to learning to control the body and its experiences, few exercises can beat the over-3,000-year-old practice of yoga."

~Sharon Heller From
Too Loud, too Bright, too Fast, too Tight

Better posture from yoga. Better focus. Better balance. Stronger muscles. Stronger core. Stronger nervous system! The list goes on.

Yoga asanas stimulate and integrates all the senses, enhancing sensory integration. They do so by providing antigravity control, postural control, midline development, core control, coordination, body awareness, modulation and regulation of breath.

Proprioception comes from balancing and weight bearing postures, changing body positions, and postures involving push/pull (flexion/extension) into joints and muscles ("heavy work"). All put pressure into the joint. This pressure sends information to the brain about where the body is in space to enhance body awareness.

Vestibular input happens with each head change as you move through space in different directions: upright, forward, backward, rotated—from up to down; from backbends to forward bends; from bends to twists. These head changes tap into the balance system and alert the brain to change of position to maintain balance and perspective. Upside down poses especially enact a huge vestibular surge. If you find that a morning class consisting of headstands, handstands, Crow, and Firefly in Power Vinyasa yoga effectively settles you throughout the day, thank the vestibular hits.

Deep pressure touch, the most calming form of input—think bear hug!—comes from bare feet pushing into floor or mat; hands pressed into various parts of the body for support; the instructor's physical adjustments;

(Judy)

a fellow student's body pushed into yours in partner yoga;

(Judy & Partner)

or just playing around.

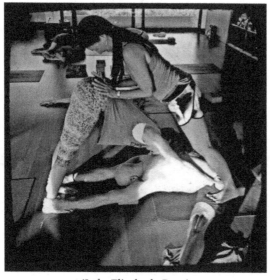

(Judy, Elizabeth, Ryan)

Deep pressure in floor poses like Savasana or lying prone on the belly increases sensory input across large surface areas of the body enhancing body awareness.

To bolster the calming effect of deep pressure touch, the sweat itself that pours down your body harkens back to the soothing wet warmth of the womb.

Visual input comes from seeing the poses demonstrated and imitating them, from dristi (focus) as you balance, and from noticing what your body is doing. "Notice if your knee if over your foot," teachers will tell you in the extended leg in Warrior I.

Auditory input comes from yoga instructions, from description of what's taking place in the body, and from inspiring aphorisms throughout a spiritually oriented yoga class. It comes as well from music playing, from hearing your breathing, and from chanting in classes like Kundalini yoga.

In addition to the postures, pranayama (yoga breathing), mudra (gestures practiced with hands and fingers) and meditation all have a soothing and regulatory effect on the nervous system.

As another plus, yoga practice can be adapted to a variety of ages, learning styles and environments to get a body moving.

Here are the many ways in which yoga naturally employs sensory integration principles to enhance the functioning of all.

Muscle Development & Movement

Take the path of the least resistance by taking the path of the least movement was my mother's mantra. She had low muscle tone and moving her body took effort—9x more effort, discovered pediatric OTs for those with floppy bodies than those with firm muscle tone. Not only did she never exercise, she designed her life to remain stationary. If the phone rang or the doorbell chimed, she yelled for one of her children to answer. If the dog needed walking or the garbage thrown out, she yelled for us to do the chore.

"Lazy" I called her. When I learned about SPD, I changed "lazy" to "low muscle tone" and my heart filled with sympathy for what life must have been inside her body; a body with weak muscle development; a body out of touch with the pleasure of movement; an obese body that later in life waddled and warranted a call to the paramedics to pick her up from the ground when she fell.

How Yoga Helps

To move your body against gravity, to stabilize your body, to help it resist change, or to sense or feel (proprioceive) your body requires muscles.

Yoga asanas stretch and use all muscles groups in the body. This holistic input builds the muscles needed to resist gravity; extends range of motion for joints; creates flexibility; and enhances sequencing and planning of movement (praxis). Weight bearing poses, like inversions and balancing on one leg or arms especially force you to use muscles against gravity because your own body weight is pushed into the ground.

Whoever said yoga was a simple stretch class!

Importantly, asanas build core. Your body has 29 core muscles located mostly in your back, abdomen and pelvis. The stronger one's core, the better control you have over your body, even fine motor skills. Yoga builds core because the poses involve multi-planar, multi-joint movements that place demand on the body's core musculature, strengthening them. This protects and supports your back, makes your spine and body less prone to injury, as well as helping you gain greater balance and stability.

Bandhas

The first time a yoga teacher told the class to use *Mula Bandha* during Downward-Facing-Dog, I shook my head. What's that? In yoga, you don't typically raise your hand to ask a question as talking interrupts concentration and flow. You just plug away. Later, I found out that *Mula Bandha* meant basically squeezing your anus shut.

Bandhas, of which there are several, contract muscle groups to provide a lock or seal. This seal stabilizes, strengthens and energizes the poses, as well as increasing stillness and awareness of the body.

As you flow through Sun Salutations, (a sequence starting in Mountain and flowing Forward Bend, Plank, Upward-Facing Dog, Downward-Facing dog and other poses), two energy locks, Mula Bandha and Uddiyana Bandha help build core: *Mula Bandha* refers to pulling in and or contracting of the pelvic floor muscles to stabilize the pelvis and is used in conjunction with asanas; *Uddiyana Bandha* refers to contraction of the upper abdominal area and is used in conjunction with pranayama.

Using your Bandhas takes conscious awareness and intention and forces you to focus on the present and what's going on inside your body. When starting yoga, I would glance in the mirror in Child Pose and see my back arched and my "tushy" sticking out. Not much core there. Not much use of Bandhas. Today, I'm more conscious of using especially Mula Bandha and I'm in more of a rounded fetal tuck in Child.

While using Bandhas takes much practice and concentration, and many skip it, especially in a more basic Hatha Yoga class, doing so is necessary for core stabilization. Without core, you can't do more challenging poses like inversions and weight bearing poses and you may miss out on a deeper experience of yoga bliss.

Muscle Control & Balance

When I first began yoga practice with Bikram yoga, a strenuous practice that repeats the same 26 poses in a humid, hot 105° room, I still had muscles and a relatively strong dancer's body. Moving deliberately, I sculpted my body into the posture and moved easily into the pose, loving the challenge of balancing like the dancer I once was.

Following head trauma, my muscles gradually weakened. Weakness was exacerbated further by malnourishment from extreme food sensitivities that stemmed from 30 years of candida overgrowth (a result of long-term antibiotics when young). My formerly fit and firm body transformed into a wet noodle and felt like a lump of flesh. Weak and thin, my yoga teacher nicknamed me "bony marony."

My yoga practice became an unsteady challenge and I wavered in balance poses I had managed before, like tree or Warrior III. I switched to a more basic hatha yoga class that required less strength and endurance, content to twist and turn while collapsed on the floor. Practicing once or twice a week was all I could handle.

After a regimen of raw food and detoxifying, along with a barrage of other therapies, my body slowly rejuvenated. In addition to yoga, I ate whole, organic, non-allergenic food to feed my brain the nutrition it needed to boost my system; took amino acid supplements like Taurine, along with GABA (the body's natural valium) to calm; dabbed daily pure essentials oils on my skin for greater emotional stability; did syntonic light therapy for visual processing issues; used the CHI machine for circulation and muscle relaxation; and did body rolling for aching muscles.

If I went off my strict regimen and, for instance, ate too many carbohydrates, had caffeine, or one of the dozen of foods to which I was intolerant, I would be at once wired and exhausted during class and struggle throughout to stay above water. Much of the class I spent in Child Pose. My warm, loving teacher would come over to give me a few back rubs and ask if I was okay. She thought I was in pain. I would just nod. That was easier than explaining adrenal exhaustion!

Slowly, my body strengthened and I began practicing Power Vinyasa yoga at a nearby health club in Boca Raton. Invented by two American yogis, Beryl Bender Birch and Bryan Kest, the addictive practice is now taught in most yoga studios in the US and throughout the world.

Practicing three to four days a week religiously, I developed better musculature slowly and, with it improved balance. Giving me the most bliss, Power Vinyasa has remained my main yoga practice.

How Yoga Helps

All standing yoga poses require balance, as do entry in and out of the poses. To balance, you must pay attention to how your body feels (interoception) and what it's doing (kinesthesia) to sense when you're going out of alignment. When you start to waver, you shift your body to reinstate alignment.

Balancing would be hard without muscles, as you need muscles to resist gravity. The more you improve balance, the stronger your muscles become, making yoga a strength building practice. At least one small study, published in The Journal of Strength and Conditioning Research in 2013 concurs. The study compared eight weeks of Bikram yoga with no intervention in 32 young, healthy, adults. Results showed that the yoga classes improved deadlift strength.

This won't surprise serious yogis. Consider the muscle control needed to stay steady in the Dancer.

(Jen)

Or the muscle control needed to balance on your buttocks in Boat Pose.

(Jen)

Not easy.

Yoga provides muscle control because your body serves as the weights you would use in weight and strength training. Lifting your leg to balance on one leg in Tree is the same as lifting a 26 lb. weight, the weight of the average leg. "In trying handstand, I felt as if my legs each weighed 100 pounds," writes Claire Dederer in *Poser, my life in twenty-three yoga poses.*

Or to balance on the hand and the side of your foot in Side Plank.

(Judy)

Lift your arms over your head in extended Mountain and you are lifting around 16 pounds over your head, as 8 lb. is the average weight of arm. In a difficult pose like this Flying Split Arm Balance, you add the weight of your whole body.

(Ryan)

To build muscle, strength and flexibility, yoga teachers advise at least three classes a week regularly, over time.

A caveat. If you practice simple Hatha yoga, where you're lying down or sitting for much of the time, your balance won't improve. You must do a level of yoga where you are upright much of the class for the practice to have any real effect on balance.

Muscles & Body Awareness

My neighbor Sarah has floppy, low muscle tone and weak musculature. Her arms hang limp from her shoulder sockets; her legs paddle as she walks. Clumsy and uncoordinated, with poor posture and poor balance, she controls musculature with effort, and moving her body feels more like moving arms and legs than moving a solid structure. "As a child, I moved like a monkey," she says in self-deprecating humor.

If you lack good musculature, you are out of touch with

ILLUMINATING

KINESTHESIA VS. PROPRIOCEPTION

Though proprioception and kinesthesia tend to be thought of as the same there is a distinct difference. Knowing your hand is about to touch a hot stove is proprioception; the sensation of pulling your hand away is kinesthesia. In other words kinesthesia refers to how your brain interprets proprioceptive information —to proprioceptive awareness. In yoga, kinesthesia keys you into how you are moving your body in and out of poses as well as stabilizing your body in poses.

---

your body and controlling movement is arduous; you live inside your body as if living in a stranger's suit. Poor proprioception and poor kinesthesia, the latter the sensation of the awareness of your body moving in space are the culprits.

To get acquainted with your body you must build muscle. Without doing so, you lack the facility to *feel* your body and to control your body against gravity. Remember, the purpose of muscles is to allow you to move against gravity. Without strong muscles, you live unsteadily in space, and both physical and emotional security eludes you.

How Yoga Helps

Yoga asanas push against gravity. This push takes strength and builds muscles. As strength builds, proprioception improves and with it body awareness. The more body awareness, the more grounded you feel, enabling you to continue or to hold movement in an asana far longer with proper form.

There are psychological benefits as well. The more grounded you are, the safer you feel moving through the world. The feeling of being connected to the earth gives you a sense of self as whole and present, stabilizing and comforting you. Your brain streams with alpha brains waves, the brain state that allows you to feel the stability of solid earth and to feel present.

> *"The nature of yoga is to shine the light of awareness into the darkest corners of the body."*
>
> ~JASON CRANDELL

What does feeling grounded mean? This exercise by Alexander Lowen, the creator of bioenergetics, a system that works with body and breath to release emotions will shed light. Stand with your feet about eight inches apart, knees slightly bent, and reach out as if to shake someone's hand. At the same time, press the corresponding foot into the ground and lean forward slightly as you extend your arm. You should feel the movement extending from the ground up through your arm and a lifting and elongating through your center.

Body Awareness & Internal Sensation

In addition to poor body awareness, my neighbor Sarah has poor *internal* awareness of sensation. She eats compulsively because she doesn't sense when she's satiated. She suffers constipation because she doesn't sense when she needs to defecate. She is unaware she has cut her finger because she doesn't sense pain easily. Once she fractured a vertebra in her lumbar spine from a car accident. The pain tolerable, she didn't go to the doctor for weeks. That she handled the pain astounded the surgeon who performed her back surgery.

Sarah has poor *interoception,* our "eighth" sense and the sense that puts us in tune with the inner workings of our body.

About Interoception

"The current human disconnection from the natural world starts with our disconnection from our own bodies, which we as a culture inherited – to a degree that most of us generally don't quite acknowledge the extent of our inability to feel our own bodies."

~Simon Thakur

Connected to our internal organs are nerve endings that send signals to the brain. This allows us to interpret inner, physical states and to know if we're hungry or satiated, hot or cold, alert or fatigued, needing to urinate or defecate, tense or relaxed, in pain or just experiencing uncomfortable sensation.

Interoception links us to our gut feelings, our inner intuition that tells us "Go for it!" or "Pull back." It is the recognition of and response to momentary sensations in the body as they fluctuate in time that allows us to identify tension ("Pull back.") or relaxation ("Go for it!).

Such awareness gives us the opportunity to stop and reset to maintain *homeostasis*: our balanced state. This in turn fosters better sensory modulation and translates into more adaptive and functional behavior. Ultimately, a more integrated and solid sense of self emerges, more cohesive and coherent in time and space. Little wonder so many die-hard yogis describe the practice as life transforming.

"Yoga practice can make us more and sensitive to subtler and subtler sensations in the body. Paying attention to and staying with finer and finer sensations within the body is one of the surest ways to steady the wandering mind."

~ RAVI RAVINDRA

Hyper- & Hypo-sensitive

People vary in their sensitivity to interoception, based on sensitivity.

The hyposensitive, like Sarah fail to notice changes in breathing, heart rate, muscle tension and pain and proceed blind. This lack of awareness not only disconnects you from your body but can result in you failing to take the necessary actions to calm, balance, and reset when destabilized. In yoga, you are more likely to push through a posture and risk injury.

Conversely, those more acutely aware of sensations out in the world, like me are also more sensitive to internal cues, like a pounding heart. With such awareness, I'm better able to recognize when it's time to take a break and give my body a chance to relax and my mind to quiet. During yoga, I might stop to take a sip of water or lay down and pull into the calming fetal tuck of Child's Pose.

Still, such awareness is not easy, it takes constant concentration. In Half Bow Pose in Anuttara Raja, a style of yoga focused on stretching fascia (similar to Yin Yoga), I often find myself incorrectly tightening my glute muscles in my extended leg, even when focused on what my body is doing. Fortunately, Philip keeps reminding us. "Feel any tightness in your glutes," he will invariably say during the pose.

How Yoga Helps

Paying attention to internal sensation is a major focus in yoga. You do so by consciously noticing pain, numbness, or tingling; tightness in the chest; or other internal sensations as you flow through the asanas. You pay particular attention to the breath, and how you are breathing (fast, slow, shallow, deep). Such awareness connects you to your body and trains your mind to take control of your body, and more fully inhabit it.

"Body speaks. Listen to your body," says Judy.

Verbal Reminders

To increase interoception and better inhabit your body, yoga teachers will urge you to feel what your body's doing.

"Feel roots of fingers," says James while we're in Downward-Facing Dog in Vinyasa. "Keep weight in the root of the big toes."

They will encourage you to pay attention to whether a muscle is activating, stretching, or relaxing; to notice sensation of pressure and tightness, tingling and throbbing; to detect any discomfort such as from overextending your muscles or torqueing your knees, common in lotus pose.

(Daja)

"Back off," they will caution, as you never want to feel discomfort or, worse, pain in your knees.

You learn to pay attention to whether your belly is rising and falling with each breath to know if your breathing is deep or shallow. Or notice if your heart is racing and it's time to take a break in Child's Pose to settle and re-organize.

You learn to notice the differences between the two sides of the body, how each side feels before a pose and immediately after a posture. Through paying attention to both sides of my body in asanas, I became aware of how weak my right side was compared to my left, due to scoliosis, and worked consciously to put more weight into my right side.

Body Scan

Another way to boost interoception is to do a body scan during Savasana. By letting your awareness travel the length and breadth of your body, you notice the tension, heaviness, or relaxation in your muscles and consciously relax.

Holding Poses

The longer you hold the poses, the more time you have to attend to what's going inside your body and attend to the sensation. In Anuttara Raja and Iyengar, where we can hold a pose for as long as five minutes, I have more time to adjust my body properly into a straight spine position with weight equal on both sides.

Motor Planning & Coordination

"Right leg out. Feet turned at an angle. Extend right arm. Drop right hand to right shin. I started to worry. How was I going to get that left arm up? How was I going to turn my torso?" So writes Dederer in her engaging and at times hilarious memoir, "*Poser, my life in twenty-three yoga poses*," as she tries to follow a yoga tape.

Claire was experiencing some *dyspraxia*.

Praxis is the body's ability to plan movement to allow you to coordinate movement while moving through a sequence of unfamiliar body movements. *Dyspraxia* is the inability to do so with ease. Slight dyspraxia was another factor in my inability to follow dance steps.

How Yoga Helps

Bending, twisting, balancing on hands or legs, and stretching though the asanas fosters praxis. It does so by enhancing smoothness of movement and dexterity, as well as improving gross motor planning skills to better determine how to get in and out of a position gracefully.

Also helping with praxis is breaking down postures into the smallest components, as well-trained yoga teachers do.

For instance, to get into Happy Baby the teacher might say: "Lay on your back. Draw your knees into your chest. Grab the outside of each foot with its relevant hand. Keeping the inner thighs close to the outer ribs, draw your shoulder blades down your back and flush with the floor. Curl the tailbone into the floor. Open the knee angle to 90degree making the sole of each foot face the ceiling. Let the weight of the arms draw the knees deeper into the floor by the armpits, your whole back as well as your hips remain in contact with the floor."

As you repeat the sequence over and over, praxis improves and it becomes easier to do the poses fluidly. In other words, if you stick with it, yoga will make you less of a clutz.

Bilateral Coordination

One of the diagnostic activities occupational therapist Patti Oetter gave me to do at the Ayres clinic in California was to walk in the infinity circle. She threw two large tires on the floor, parallel to each other and around two feet apart, and told me to walk around them in a figure 8 without touching the tires.

When turning to the right, my body leaned in easily and I walked smoothly. When switching to the left to turn the circle, I hesitated and faltered.

"Hmmm," Patti uttered. "Some problem with bilateral coordination."

Part of having praxis is having good *bilateral coordination,* meaning you use equally both sides of the body. With good bilateral integration/coordination both sides of the brain communicate effectively and share information. An example in yoga is bringing the palms together.

That I had a problem with bilateral coordination surprised me. I had been a dancer and taught to use both sides of my body equally. Why would I have difficulty in coordinating both sides of my body?

Then I remembered what a chiropractor had told me in my early 30's. After giving me a kinesthetic test, he said the muscles on the right side of my body were weak. Really? I'd never noticed. When I got home, I looked in the mirror. What I saw astonished me. When I covered the right side of my body with my right arm, I saw a firm, well defined left hip and thigh. When I covered the left side of my body with my left arm, I saw a somewhat flabby, ill-defined right hip and thigh.

Well, I'll be. Perhaps that's why coordinating movement when dancing took slight effort and concentration, and why I had minor, barely detectable, yet undeniable stiffness when dancing.

After my fall down the stairs, coordinating movement of both sides of my body became a terrific challenge. While my dancer's body had felt as if gliding through butter, it now felt as if I were swimming through sludge when I danced, or tried to.

I had the unique experience of having normal body tone and musculature on my left side, which felt fluid and graceful, and weak, low tone musculature on my right side, which felt awkward and stiff. It was as if the right and left side of my body resided in a different universe: left side firm and strong; right side lumpy and weak. This difference gave me insight into what clumsy, uncoordinated people with low muscle tone and weak musculature experience daily.

As a result of my weak right side, I had constant aching muscles in my legs because I used my left leg more than my right. My right foot was supinated, leaning to the right. This caused plantar fasciitis and pain throughout my feet. Kalso Earth exerciser sandals were the only shoes I could comfortably wear. When I wrote a screenplay that got some attention, I fantasied about receiving an Oscar and boldly strolling up to the stage in dressy Earth sandals.

In addition to foot pain, I experienced pain in both knees; pain in my hips with sciatica on my left side; tendinitis in both wrists; a frozen shoulder in each shoulder (fortunately at different times); and TMJ in my jaw. Without yoga to build muscle and stretch me out, I would need to be drugged on Oxycontin to get out of bed.

Over time, NCR and yoga balanced my body more and today I suffer only slight weakness on the right side. Better able to coordinate dance steps, I've rediscovered the joy of dance.

A Split Brain

By preventing the two sides of the brain from communicating well, poor bilateral coordination affected me in other ways than movement. It affected my vision and hearing as well.

I love color meditation tapes that go through the body's chakras by having you envision the color going from the top of your head down your body. In my mind, I see the color on just one side of my body, my left side. To try and conjure the color on my right side takes great concentration and ruins the whole idea of being present.

Something similar happens with hearing. While I'm right handed, I hold the phone in my left hand always as discerning the message through my right ear takes great concentration.

How Yoga Helps

Yoga uses both sides of body because all poses are done on both the right and left side.

Yoga also encourages bilateral integration by using both sides of the body simultaneously, as in Eagle.

(Judy)

Crossing the Midline

My neighbor Sarah has always been clumsy and avoided dancing. When she does dance, she barely extends an arm from one side of her body to the other. Rather, the arm gets stuck awkwardly in the middle. Low muscle tone and poor bilateral integration makes it difficult for her to *cross the midline.*

Crossing the midline is the ability to reach across the body to the opposite side with your arms and legs and is part of good bilateral coordination as well as praxis. The midline is an invisible line dividing the body in half. When a leg or an arm from one half of the body crosses over to the other half of the body this is crossing the midline.

This helps the brain communicate in greater depth by connecting both halves of the brain via the corpus callosum, the network of fibers that divides the brain. The greater the integration of the two sides of the brain the greater the speed, flexibility, adaptability and depth of the brain's thinking.

Clumsy people with poor body awareness frequently find crossing the midline of the body a challenge. Everyday tasks such as writing, dressing, dancing and sports like hitting a ball with a racket in tennis take concentration and effort.

How Yoga Helps

Yoga practice is replete with poses that require crossing the midline of the body to help with bilateral integration, especially twists that involve crossing the arms like Eagle.

Persisting in these poses trains the two sides of the body to communicate better and accords well with the notion of yoga as union. In Hatha yoga, Yoga means "to yoke," while Hatha means the energies of the body ("ha" refers to the right side of the body, to the sun's energy and vigor; "tha" refers to the left side, to the moon and passivity). Hatha yoga means yoking these two energies together, what some refer to as yin/yang, or masculine/feminine. In sensory integration parlance, we call it *bilateral coordination*.

Concentration & Focus

One of the most debilitating results of head trauma was extreme spaciness. My head filled with cotton candy.

It wasn't a new state. Because of the auditory and visual processing problems I had suffered all my life, I had always been a space cadet and lived my childhood as if in a trance. Now, the head fog intensified tenfold and my constantly fuzzy brain interfered in every aspect in my life, from managing to rise, dress, and prepare breakfast without walking in circles to teaching a class of undergraduate psychology students without sounding like a blithering idiot.

A few days after *Too Loud, too Bright* was published I had 40 or so radio interviews, as well as an interview with NBC news. In a panic, I called my editor, Gail Winston.

"I can't do it. I'll blank out," I told her.

It took an hour 3-way phone call with Gail and my agent to convince me to do the interviews. Somehow, I only blanked out during two of the interviews. Unfortunately, one was with NCR, perhaps the most important radio show. I was mortified.

It took years of cranial therapy and yoga for the cobwebs to dissipate, though I will never be one of those people who thinks *on their feet*.

How Yoga Helps

Yoga practice is the art of focus. To improve proprioception, balance, and body awareness, you need to sense and focus on what your body is doing in the pose. If not and your mind wanders, you will waiver and may even fall.

Take what happened to me one morning when doing a headstand on a yoga stool.

As I started to bend my body from the waist and slowly descend, I thought about how much core was needed to maintain the descent. Flop! I fell out of it and nearly slumped to the ground. By losing focusing on what my body was doing, I lost my balance.

Balance. It's not just staying steady on your feet but staying steady in life. Let's explore.

RECAP

Yoga asanas stimulate and integrates all the senses, enhancing sensory integration.

Proprioception: comes from balancing and weight bearing postures, changing body positions, and postures involving push/pull (flexion/extension) into joints and muscles ("heavy work").

Vestibular Input: happens with each head change as you move through space in different directions: upright, forward, backward, rotated—from up to down; from backbends to forward bends; from bends to twists.

Deep Pressure Touch: comes from bare feet pushing into floor or mat; hands pressed into various parts of the body for support; the instructor's physical adjustments.

Visual Input: comes from seeing the poses demonstrated and imitating them, from dristi (focus) as you balance, and from noticing what your body is doing.

Auditory Input: comes from yoga instructions, from description of what's taking place in the body, and from inspiring aphorisms throughout a spiritually oriented yoga class.

Ways in which yoga naturally employs sensory integration principles to enhance the functioning of all.

Muscle Development & Movement: Yoga asanas stretch and use all muscles groups in the body. Importantly, asanas build core.

Bandhas: Bandhas contract muscle groups to provide a lock or seal. This seal stabilizes, strengthens and energizes the poses, as well as increasing stillness and awareness of the body.

Muscle Control & Balance: Yoga provides muscle control because your body serves as the weights you would use in weight and strength training.

Muscles & Body Awareness: Yoga asanas push against gravity. This push takes strength and builds muscles. As strength builds, proprioception improves and with it body awareness.

Body Awareness & Internal Sensation: Paying attention to internal sensation is a major focus in yoga. You do so by consciously noticing pain, numbness, or tingling; tightness in the chest; or other internal sensations as you flow through the asanas. You pay particular attention to the breath, and how you are breathing (fast, slow, shallow, deep).

> **Hyposensitive:** fail to notice changes in breathing, heart rate, muscle tension and pain and proceed blind.

> **Hypersensitive:** more sensitive to internal cues, like a pounding heart.

Motor Planning & Coordination: In yoga, bending, twisting, balancing on hands or legs, and stretching though the asanas fosters praxis, the body's ability to plan movement to allow you to coordinate movement while moving through a sequence of unfamiliar body movements. It does so by enhancing smoothness of movement and dexterity, as well as improving gross motor planning skills to better determine how to get in and out of a position gracefully.

Bilateral Coordination: Yoga uses both sides of body because all poses are done on both the right and left side. Yoga also encourages bilateral integration by using both sides of the body simultaneously.

Crossing the Midline: Crossing the midline is the ability to reach across the body to the opposite side with your arms and legs. It is part of good bilateral coordination, as well as praxis. Yoga practice is replete with poses that require crossing the midline of the body to help with bilateral integration, especially twists that involve crossing the arms like Eagle and Noose Pose.

Concentration & Focus: Yoga practice is the art of focus. To improve proprioception, balance, and body awareness, you need to sense and focus on what your body is doing in the pose. If not and your mind wanders, you will waiver and may even fall.

CHAPTER 3

FINDING MIDDLE GROUND

"Balance is a feeling derived from being whole and complete; it's a sense of harmony. It is essential to maintaining quality in life and work."

~JOSHUA OSENGA,
12 YEARS A CUBICLE SLAVE

I was born emotional, feeling overly excited pleasure and overly deep sorrow. I laugh quickly. I tear quickly.

Even as a young child, my senses were acute. My mother spoke of how I winced my nose at her perfume.

Such extreme emotions and sensitivity to the world has made my life an on-going see-saw, too high up, too low down, with precious little time spent quietly on stable, even ground. How I envy those who live steadily in the middle!

Like Goldie Locks, we want the world to be neither too hot nor too cold but just right. We want to feel neither hopelessly sad nor wild with pleasure. In sensory integration parlance, we want to be *modulated*.

That I get myself to the mat year after year has much to do with how it makes me more modulated. During yoga practice, the ground feels stable and sure and my emotions stay steady and calm *most of the time.*

SENSORY MODULATION

Brain Network for Sensory Modulation

Sensory modulation is the ability to turn up or turn down the volume of sensory input; to focus in on and respond appropriately to relevant sensation. With a modulated nervous system, indicating good sensory integration, the sensory threshold is set neither too low nor too high and you are even-tempered and adaptable. With an unmodulated nervous system, indicating poor sensory integration, you feel overstimulated and avoid additional sensation, or feel under-stimulated and seek excessive sensation.

RAS: Reticulating Activation System

How aroused you are by sensation starts in the reticulating activating system (RAS) in the brainstem. Directly fed by the vestibular system, the RAS is responsible for revving up or calming down the system. It regulates arousal by balancing arousal levels and setting the sensory threshold: slow, rhythmic movement calms; fast or irregular movement alerts.

Thalamus

Located just above the brainstem, the thalamus serves as the sensory switchboard. Involving the balance of glutamate, the excitatory neurotransmitter and GABA, the "chill" neurotransmitter to dampen overexcitement, the thalamus sends sensory impulses, through alpha waves to the amygdala for sensory appraisal and to the neocortex at the top of the brain. The thinking brain interprets the kinesthetic awareness of your body stretched forward in Seated Wide Forward Fold as pleasurable, and the discomfort of bending backwards in Camel as frightening.

In those who are hypersensitive to sensation, too little of the regulator GABA in the brain sends sensory information unfiltered through the thalamus, causing a traffic jam, and flooding the brain with too much information all at once.

How Yoga Helps

Yoga, through intense somatosensory input (deep pressure touch and proprioception) in the asanas, conscious breathing, and focus on the present moment and bodily sensation inhibits this flood of information. This inhibition improves sensory filtering in the thalamus.

Modulating neurotransmitters released during yoga asanas and conscious breathing, like serotonin, and release of endorphins move you out of the sympathetic flight/fight system and into the calming parasympathetic system to restore homeostasis (self-regulation).

Yoga philosophy itself encourages sensory withdrawal. In fact, one of the eight limbs of Ashtanga from the *Yoga Sutras* is sensory withdrawal—*Pratahara*.

ILLUMINATING

The yoga bible, Patanjali's Yoga Sutras, a definitive yoga reference, describe yoga as a system for attaining "undisturbed calmness of mind." It consists of 8 limbs of practice:

YAMA - Ethics

NIYAMA – Virtuous Behaviors

ASANA - Posture

PRANAYAMA - Breath

PRATYHARA - Sense withdrawal

DHARANA - Concentration

DHYANA - Meditation

SAMADHI - Bliss or enlightenment

Some poses especially foster sensory withdrawal, like Child Pose, Savasana, and, my favorite the restorative "Sleeping Serpent" pose (lying on belly). Not only are you lying in stillness but the eyes are closed and that increases alpha brain waves.

As our dominant sense for learning about the world, vision accounts for 80% of the information we take in. Keeping eyes closed shuts out distracting sensory stimulation, and keeps you centered and focused inward, encouraging interoception.

Yoga is perhaps the only physical activity that permits closing eyes as you practice. More spiritually oriented classes, like Anuttara Raja encourage keeping eyes closed throughout the practice.

Except in postures requiring balance, I tend to keep my sensitive eyes closed in all my classes, even in Power Vinyasa. To my annoyance, my Iyengar teachers keep telling me to open my eyes during class. Apparently some Iyengar teachers believe that when the eyes are closed you might tune out.

Better Modulated

The longer I've practiced yoga, the more modulated I've become. My reaction to noise is an example.

Yoga South is located on the corner in a small strip of light commercial/industrial property. In the desire to keep the studio warm and our muscles warm, James eschews air conditioning for keeping the windows and the garage door that leads into the studio open. Noise from outside is unavoidable: cars whizzing by; the roar of a truck engine bringing in supplies; the neighbor's electric saw as he makes repairs; landscapers; car alarm. When unnerving sound intrudes, James will joke about the excessive noise as a test of our ability to concentrate and focus. And he's right.

At my worst, I became murderous when the leaf blowers were outside the window and would leave class to scream at them to stop. Today, I can focus on my practice and shut out the mayhem for the most part. I'm amazed at how I can tune out even the beeping of a truck backing up which produces typically 1000 Hz pure tone beeps at 97-112 decibels, a high-pitched sound that drives most up the wall.

Stress Response

Stress!!! With the technological hijacking of our lives, information overload, and speeded up days, it's hard to unwind; many live their lives wired, tense and anxious.

Our bodies were designed to run furiously from danger or fight back mightily, expending enormous energy and releasing stress chemicals like cortisol. Afterward you feel better.

But when the threat is not a raging tiger but rush hour traffic, fifty emails to answer, or the nasty comments about you on social media there's nowhere to run to and no one to punch. You just sit and stew. Without release, these stress chemicals within the body become toxic and excess energy gets stored in our limbs. The less modulated you are, the less adaptable you are to stress and the greater the likelihood of not recovering from a stressful event.

How Yoga Helps

Yoga provides an outlet to release tension and increase modulation.

Slowing Down the Brain

During a yoga session, certain parts of your brain, specifically the frontal lobe and parietal lobe slow down to allow them to rest.

The frontal lobe is the thinking part of the brain that races when you're confronted with a dilemma or threat. By getting you into your body and out of the thinking mode, yoga helps your brain relax.

The parietal lobe is a sensory and motor strip across the top of the scalp. It's the section of the brain that handles all the information coming from your senses: sights, sounds, smells, touches and everything else you observe around you. In our loud, thumping, ear-splitting, crowded, constantly moving, brightly lit world the nervous system can barely take a breather. By staying present and focusing on sensations in the body, yoga slows down processing in the parietal lobe.

Releasing Tension

Asanas stretch, lengthen, and balance the muscles and release built-up muscle tension and stiffness throughout the body. The result is reduced overexcitement, irritability and anxiety, and more resilient bodies and minds better equipped to handle stress.

Science concurs. An NHIS study found 80 percent of people practicing yoga in the US to experience less stress than before starting the practice. Eighty percent! That's huge.

In a 2005 study, German researchers found that women wrestling with mental illness reported less stress and fatigue after three months of regular yoga classes. After one session of yoga, comprehensive tests showed even the subjects' saliva contained less cortisol.

Creating Stress

Another reason to hit the mat is because yoga *creates* stress. Under certain circumstances, stress has a favorable effect and is a good thing.

How could this be?

Discomfort and disorientation trigger the stress response. And there's plenty of that in yoga. The disorientation and uneasiness when upside down; the twisting of spine, lactic acid building up in laboring muscles; the strained breath as you hold Dancer. And then you come down from the headstand, straighten out from the seated twist, and stand back on two feet from Dancer. The exertion relaxes, and the massive chemical release transforms "I hate yoga," to "I love yoga."

How modulated and self-regulated are you? Let's Explore.

Modulated and Adaptive

Tiny and thin, with long flaxen blond hair that shimmers in the sunlight, Jen is an advanced yogi who practices daily and has for years.

Calm, cool and collected, she typifies a modulated nervous system. Whether the room is light or dark, warm or cool, noisy or quiet matters little, as she adapts easily to most circumstances.

While not liking bright lights, as her light blue eyes are naturally light sensitive she will tolerate nevertheless sitting under a naked lightbulb.

Sound is also not an issue. A while ago, James stopped using music in class, as he feels it interferes with focusing on breath. For Jen and others in the class, music or no music makes no difference.

Avoiders, Seekers, Cravers

Avoiders

Wired and anxious, I become easily over-aroused.

After head trauma and before neurocranial therapy and much yoga, I was a snapping turtle and went into a tizzy at the drop of a hat. Family and friends avoided me. Once in Bikram yoga, I snapped at my yoga teacher for insisting I do Awkward Pose (a plié pose with legs parallel) as I felt it put too much pressure on my knees. Yoga teachers are gurus and nobody is EVER disrespectful in class!

Far more adaptable and modulated now, I rarely go over the edge. In fact, as I'm soft spoken people *assume* me calm!

Still, whether the room is light or dark, warm or cool, noisy or quiet matters and I have to work to temper sensation during practice.

Visual

Light sensitive, I place my mat where there's the least light, usually in the corner or on the side of the class.

Anything that I see creeping into *my* space distracts me, like water bottles, towels, or shirts, and I sit where I have enough personal space as a barrier against such intrusions.

I also steer far from anyone in my view wearing wild clothing or practicing on a wild colored mat, as my sensitive eyes finds patterns overstimulating. One day, Elizabeth, one of my teachers, was practicing next to me in Vinyasa and wearing snake patterned tights. I went crazy and kept my eyes shut the whole class. After class, we had a laugh about it and she promised not to sit next to me when wearing her snake tights.

Another time, in Iyengar yoga I was practicing next to someone whose mat had a leaf and flower pattern. While not a wild pattern, my eyes went crazy nevertheless as my artist's eyes kept seeing eyes and eyelashes, making focusing on my body impossible.

The mat itself could have been a Rorschach test. While the owner of the mat saw it as "flowers," Stephanie, my teacher saw it as "Peacock feathers." Another testament to how each of us perceives the sensory world uniquely.

Sound or No Sound

As much as I love James' class, a class without music feels lifeless to me: "something's missing," says my brain. Around halfway through the class though I've adapted to the silence and it no longer bothers me. This happens around the time that I've described a shift in my nervous system and stress dissipates.

But I will take no music to the pounding music younger people like to groove to in Power Vinyasa yoga (we'll talk more about this in chapter 9). I prefer soft New Age Music playing in the background.

Pace & Rhythm

Easily overstimulated people like me prefer and require predictable, rhythmic, slow movement, as this will best move one into the parasympathetic mode. We gravitate more toward yoga classes that move slowly, like Iyengar, Yin yoga, and Anuttara Raja, where poses are held much longer than in Vinyasa, and to classes that move rhythmically like Kundalini, or predictably like Bikram.

Why then am I so addicted to Vinyasa? *No other style gives me such yoga bliss!* In truth, I move to my own rhythm and flow at a slower pace than the rest of the class, especially since I skip more difficult poses like Chattaranga.

What class you choose might depend also on mood.

Mariel Hemingway practices all sorts of styles, she says in an online article in *Yogitimes,* loving them all. One day she says she might practice the Tibetan Rights and another day do two hours of asana flow. "Iyengar, Ashtanga, Anusara, *Kundalini,* Power Yoga, and Bikram all influence my practice. I love choosing the style of yoga that best suits the needs of my day."

Seekers

Mandie is a tall, thin advanced yogi and yoga teacher, with long, purple tinted hair. On her left shoulder is a small tattoo of a rose and on her right shoulder a small tattoo of Ganesh. Outgoing and a sensation seeker, she parks her mat up front and in the middle, a place where she is noticed and sandwiched between others. Unlike avoiders, seekers want to be in the other's space as touching another adds more sensation and feels good.

Mandie's sensory threshold is set at high. Taking in too little stimuli, she's under-responsive to sensation and seeks more dopamine, the pleasure seeking hormone that taps into the brain's reward "opiate" system and drives one toward seeking excitement. Fast, unpredictable, arrhythmic, and angular inputs excite her and she enjoys yoga classes with boom boom music, to which she grooves while wearing wild patterned tights in psychedelic colors. Lack of music bores her.

Cravers

Does Mandie have sensory processing issues? Not necessarily. Sensation seeking is a normal function and usually a quality of bold, daring, risk taking leaders.

Those who have sensory processing issues are sensation "cravers." With these folks sensation dominates behavior with little control to put a brake on: always craving more, they continue to seek to where they become disorganized.

They are the ones who go over the edge and become substance abusers; who show hyperactive ADHD behavior; who get into your face when you barely know them; who get silly and make loud noises and sounds, distracting normal social interchange.

Irene might be an example of a *sensory craver.*

Fleshy and obese, Irene teaches Kundalini. Kundalini incorporates repeated movements or exercises, dynamic breathing techniques, chanting, meditation and mantras.

It looks and feels different from any other yoga classes due to its focus on repetitive, enhanced breathing intended to move energy through the body. It's also one of the few yoga styles where being fit, firm and athletic is unnecessary.

During class, Irene demonstrates a "kriya." In Kundalini you do *kriyas,* or sequences, primarily while sitting on the mat and moving parts of your body quickly side-to-side, back-and-forth, and up-and down, coordinated with specific breathing.

She doesn't do the quick, vigorous movements with us, nor does she walk around adjusting. She sits, swaying and rocking. Likely, she finds moving effortful as would fit her lack of muscle tone and weight.

The swaying and rocking helps feed her brainstem what it needs to be alert to and attend to the world. So does her speech, which she interjects with sing-song inflection in her voice. As if teaching preschoolers, her voice will vacillate from quiet to loud, from low to high-pitched, with extended syllables as if singing —"extenddd your arm reeeeellly (high note) faaaar (low note)," lots of roars, grrrrs, laughing and clapping, with an occasional British accent thrown in, "rathaaa." For her, class is entertainment. Silliness, clowning, loudness, chirping voice, guffawing—all are self-stimming to rev up her system.

Yoga is not show biz. Such behavior is counter-intuitive for yoga's goal—to focus on what's going on inside our bodies.

That she persists in engaging in such silliness indicates she lacks control to prevent it.

Benefit of Obesity

Yoga teachers take great pride in their bodies. It's highly unusual for someone who's obese to be a yoga teacher. Why wouldn't Irene put great effort into weight control? For that matter, why don't more obese people?

One reason may be that obesity itself creates grounding. Having considerable weight pushes your body into the ground to feel the earth beneath your feet. If you lose considerable weight, you feel too light and anxiously ungrounded. To regain more of a sense of being inside a solid body many gain the weight back.

On the keto diet, my fleshy neighbor Sarah lost over one hundred pounds. Her body svelte, she threw away her fat clothes and bought a new wardrobe.

"You must feel great," I said.

"Not really. I don't know how to describe it. It's an uncomfortable feeling."

"Like you'll suddenly float into the air?"

"That's it!"

Yoga's Boring!

Some adrenaline junkies never try yoga. My brother is one of them. He would be bored to tears by the repetition, dim light, and quiet music, sensations that would fail to keep his mind tuned in and alert. Full of nervous energy, he would be jumpy while lying in Child's Pose.

To engage him, he needs to be jazzed up. In his youth, he skied off the side of a mountain in Aspen thinking it a challenging jump. Luckily, he landed in a tree and eventually made his way down the mountain. Another time, he rode his motorcycle from Chicago to Los Angeles ... in winter!

Patti Oetter would flee the dark, quiet classes I love. An exceptionally calm person—"Nothing bothers me short of an atom bomb"— Patti needs intensity to engage her. As an OT for over 50 years, she loves nothing more than working with autistic children whose meltdowns keep her tuned in. After a day of therapy at Ayres Clinic in California, I asked Patti to dim the lights and turn off the music so we could talk. "If I do there will be nothing to keep *this* body going and I'll nod off."

Brain Loves Newness

To some degree, we're all sensation seekers as the brain craves novel stimuli.

Novelty and variety are the spice of life, keeping the brain young as newness rewires the brain. When confronting something new and different, our brain lights up and cerebral blood flow increases. Dopamine makes us want to explore to gain a reward. If the brain evaluates a stimulus as too familiar, it becomes uninteresting—another sunset—and we quickly habituate and lose interest.

By craving newness, we keep our inner listening skills sharp and our system remains open to take in the next new sensation. Picture the difference doing yoga inside the same studio year after year versus in a park or at the beach. Just being outside where the clouds are moving above, where the sun is lighting up the sky in brilliant reds and oranges, where the water ripples beyond my gaze titillates my senses beyond what any Zen inspired yoga studio does. Difference creates yoga bliss in spades.

Coping with Sameness

Repetition diminishes our sensing capacity because the brain knows what's coming next.

In yoga, if the routine is not varied, it becomes boring. Some drop out. This happens especially if you practice only once or twice a week, as this is not enough to change your body significantly and the class becomes hum drum.

How then does one explain Bikram yoga where, in spite of doing the same 26 poses, people flock to the classes? When Bikram first started out in Los Angeles, he became a celebrity guru and could hardly find a space large enough to accommodate the crowd.

Why would this be?

Though the poses remain the same, how you perform in the pose changes from day to day if you take class frequently.

I took Bikram yoga with gusto 3-4 days a week for around three years. Rarely was I bored because every class was new and a revelation. In Bow Pose, I would arch my back slightly more; in Tree Pose, waver slightly less; in Dancer's Pose, extend my leg back slightly higher. What a deep surge of accomplishment the day when I not only balanced in Standing Head-To-Big Toe Pose (Hasta Padangusthasana) but placed my head on my leg, without wavering. I couldn't wait to come back to class the next day.

Teaching Same Class Ad Infinitum

Still, how do Bikram teachers teach the same class week after week, year after year and not get bored to tears?

Many get burned out and seek ways to make it new and interesting. Bikram Yoga is a brand and Bikram insisted his rules be followed: No adjustments, bright lights, a carpeted floor and no music a soft carpeted floor because carpet is Some take the basic Bikram class and modify it by eliminating carpeting, adding music, and a few poses like Downward-Facing-Dog and inversions.

Burnout is a problem for most long-time yoga teachers, regardless of style. Judy, a low arousal person and long-time teacher, waves off boredom by varying sequence of poses far more than do other teachers of Vinyasa. Such unpredictability leaves you to guess what comes next and makes her classes interesting and rejuvenating; students show up in droves. In the background, she plays jazz, its arrhythmic beat keeping her engaged and interested.

To make the class more interesting, one of my teachers self-stims with constant chatter punctuated with silliness. For instance, he will say things like "let me make backup noises to help you open your hips more," and make a creaky sound, interfering with my concentration and focus.

It's annoying, at least to me though some laugh. But for him it might be necessary to keep him from nodding off.

SELF-REGULATION

Hand in hand with sensory modulation is self-regulation, the ability to keep emotions steady. Those who are modulated are emotionally even keeled. Those who are unmodulated go overboard emotionally to adapt to a situation.

If the world is too loud, too bright, *too much*, you cope by withdrawing into a shell when faced with a stressor, or go off the deep end and become a screaming Mimi.

If the world is too quiet, too dim, *too little*, you get bored in a flash. To tune in, you seek excitement by ignoring the task-at-hand, regardless of consequences, and seek addictions for an adrenaline rush. For instance, you might forget to stop and pick up fresh avocadoes to make guacamole for your guests because you got way laid in Macy's hunting for a new dress you don't need.

How well does yoga help you self-regulate? Ask the actor Robert Downey Jr., star of movies like *Tropic Thunder, Sherlock Holmes,* and *Iron Man.* A well-known drug addict—he was arrested in 2001 on drug charges—Downey thanks yoga for helping him balance and re-gain his life. He credits his miraculous comeback from the abyss to his yoga guru, his yoga teacher, Vinnie Marino, who also overcame a battle with addiction to become one of LA's most prestigious yoga teachers.

Let's now look closely at our three primary power senses, vestibular, proprioceptive and tactile, and their role in creating yoga bliss.

RECAP

SENSORY MODULATION: the ability to turn up or turn down the volume of sensory input; to focus in on and respond appropriately to relevant sensation.

BRAIN NETWORK FOR SENSORY MODULATION

Reticulating Activation System: Arousability by sensation starts in the reticulating activating system (RAS) in the brainstem. Directly fed by the vestibular system, the RAS is responsible for revving up or calming down the system.

Thalamus. Serves as the sensory switchboard. Involving the balance of glutamate, the excitatory neurotransmitter, and GABA, the "chill" neurotransmitter to dampen overexcitement, the thalamus sends sensory impulses to the amygdala in the limbic system for sensory appraisal and to the neocortex at the top of the brain.

How Yoga Helps

Sensory Modulation. Intense somatosensory input (deep pressure touch and proprioception) in the asanas, conscious breathing, and focus on the present moment and bodily sensation inhibits flood of information. Release of serotonin somatosensory input, and endorphins move you out of the sympathetic flight/ fight system and into the calming parasympathetic system to restore homeostasis (self-regulation).

Stress Response. When there's nowhere to run, as there isn't from psychological stress, stress chemicals within the body become toxic and excess energy gets stored in our limbs. Yoga provides an outlet to release tension and increase modulation.

Slows Down the Brain. During a yoga session, certain parts of your brain, specifically the frontal lobe and parietal lobe slow down to allow them to rest.

Releases Tension. Asanas stretch, lengthen, and balance the muscles and release built-up muscle tension and stiffness throughout the body. The result is reduced overexcitement, irritability and anxiety, and more resilient bodies and minds better equipped to handle stress.

LEVELS OF SENSORY MODULATION

Modulated and Adaptive. Calm, cool and collected; not easily bothered by the environment and adapts easily to most circumstances.

Avoiders. Wired and anxious and become easily over-aroused; has to work to temper sensation during practice.

Seekers. Likely to be outgoing and needing intense sensation to feel good; sensory threshold is set at high and seeks more dopamine, the pleasure seeking hormone that taps into the brain's reward "opiate" system, driving one toward excitement.

Cravers. Sensation dominates behavior with little control to put a brake on: always craving more, they continue to seek to where they become disorganized.

Brain Loves Newness. We're all sensation seekers to some degree as the brain craves novel stimuli. Novelty and variety are the spice of life, keeping the brain young as newness rewires the brain.

Coping with Sameness. Repetition diminishes our sensing capacity because the brain knows what's coming next. In yoga, if the routine is not varied, it becomes boring. Some drop out.

SELF-REGULATION. The ability to keep emotions steady. Goes hand in hand with sensory modulation: those who are modulated are emotionally even keeled; those who are unmodulated go overboard emotionally to adapt to a situation.

VESTIBULAR SENSE: STEADY ON YOUR FEET

"You watch Unus standing on one finger and you think, 'Look at such a fine, intelligent and excellent man making his living standing on one finger when most of us can't even stand on our feet.'"

~ERNEST HEMINGWAY, FROM AN ESSAY WRITTEN FOR THE PROGRAM OF THE 1953 RINGLING BROTHERS AND BARNUM & BAILEY CIRCUS

When I was 24, I toured Israel and climbed Masada's famous snake path. Starting from the base of the famous fortress that stands beside the Dead Sea, the narrow path winds its way up around 400 meters to the famous fortress of heroism and endurance. It was where in the time of King Herod over 2000 years ago zealous Jews committed suicide rather than be captured by the Romans.

The trek up Masada takes around an hour and half, and the trek down around 40 minutes. At 24, I managed the trek with bravado.

At 41, a year after experiencing head trauma, I again took the trek. *What* a harrowing experience. My sense of balance was shaky and heart pounding terror filled every second down the narrow path. Life, the *ground itself* no longer felt stable beneath my feet and that gave me a profound feeling of insecurity.

Our first *power* sense, the vestibular system is a huge player in how steady and secure we feel in our lives.

Let's explore.

ORCHESTRATOR OF THE NERVOUS SYSTEM

The vestibular system is the most sensitive of all sense organs and the first to develop in utero. Located in the inner ear, it controls sense of balance (gyroscope), orientation (compass), and movement against gravity. The system is comprised of a network of canals that detect and send information to the brain regarding gravity, linear movement and rotation. This information gives feedback of our head's position: upright, tilted, flexed, extended or rotated. Every time we move up or down, side to side, back and forth or in a circle we tap into the vestibular sense.

The vestibular system is the "unifying system" for all sensory input, impacting how we move through space to how we think and how we feel. Orchestrating the entire nervous system, it regulates muscle tone, motor control, and postural control; sequencing of movement, visual space perception, and visual-motor control; as well as auditory language skills, emotional stability, clear thinking and alertness.

If our brain receives faulty feedback from this system, dire consequences, physical, mental and emotional, result.

On Shaky Ground

One activity Patti gave me for my "sensory diet" was to walk in a pool. Walking in waist-high water, she informed me, improves balance, trains the core muscles of your abdomen, increases flexibility and boosts cardiovascular fitness. Living in Florida, this would be easy to do. I had a pool in my complex and at least ten months of sunny, warm days.

"Play music while walking and walk to the beat," said Patti.

"OK. I can do that."

"And walk backwards."

"Backwards! I've tried that. I get dizzy."

"I'm not surprised. Your vestibular system is rusty," she said. "You need to oil it."

Being at odds with gravity produces frightening physical consequences, dizziness only one. You might suffer nausea, adrenal overload, low muscle tone, tension, pain, or many other symptoms. Some people lose balance and fall easily; some experience dizziness when moving in ways that challenge the vestibular system, like tilting the head backward or moving backward; while some experience crippling vertigo, especially those that suffer Meniere's disease. It's now believed that the Dutch painter Von Gogh, who famously cut off his ear, likely did so to stop debilitating dizziness and vertigo from Meniere's disease.

Emotions and thinking take a hit as well.

Feeling starts with body sensations: feeling happy is directly proportionate to how good it feels to be inside your body. If your body is an unsteady stranger that betrays your security when navigating your world, you will get frustrated easily and hate being inside your body. Depression, anger, fear, or hostility often will result.

Mentally, unsteadiness creates confusion, disorganization, spaciness, and poor memory. Space related phobias, like fear of and heights, and even disassociation can occur as well. We'll talk more about this soon.

A Shaky World

How common is it to have a rusty vestibular system? Quite common. Estimates are that vestibular disorders occur in more than 35% of adults aged 40 or older in the US. Injury, disease, certain drugs, even the aging process itself, can put us on shaky ground.

Our society demands little in the way of movement and effectively starves our vestibular system. Sitting upright most of the day—at the computer, driving our cars, brushing our teeth, eating our meals—we experience little head change.

More or Less Vestibular Input

Do you like to swing or spin or does that make you dizzy? Do you crave roller coasters or does the mere thought of riding on Kingda Ka in New Jersey create panic? Do you love backbends in yoga class or do they make you nauseous or, even worse, terrified?

Your answer indicates whether you are hyper- or hypo-responsive to vestibular sensation.

On the Low End

Thrill seekers love the adrenaline rush of fast cars, motor boats, roller coasters, flying. You love getting your body pummeled, as when white water rafting, and defying gravity, like diving from the high board. Unable to sit still, you burst with energy. Some restless types move a body part constantly, like shaking a leg.

On the mat, you love defying gravity with lots of inversions and may enjoy Kundalini yoga with all the side-to-side, back and forth and up and down rocking and swaying.

On the High End

Thrill avoiders become quickly overloaded by vestibular input as the vestibular system tries to process too many sensations at once.

These folks will become easily car sick, sea sick and avoid roller coasters at all costs. In yoga, you might become dizzy when the head is tilted back, as in backbends, and get anxious doing the Camel.

The good news is that, over time, repeated practice in gravity defying postures will oil the vestibular system. Ice skaters who whirl around like spinning tops develop that skill from years of practice turning round and round.

Since my accident, I've had periods where I've experienced on-going dizziness. On those days, I could do very little on the mat. Today, that happens rarely and I do backbends with ease.

YOGA & VESTIBULAR INPUT

Few activities fortify the vestibular system more than hitting the mat. Many yoga asanas force you to lift your body against gravity, such as Boat, Bow, Bridge, Cobra, and Wheel.

Frequent head change occurs as you go from horizontal to vertical to angular planes while moving in and out of upright, inverted, prone, supine or sidelying positions. You get linear movement from Downward-Facing Dog to Handstand, angular from Side Plank to Triangle, and rotary in twists. Each head change lubricates the vestibular system.

Notice all the different head changes in Sun Salutation, or Surya Namaskara C (Mountain, Namaste, Backward Bend, Forward Bend, Lunge, Plank, Ashtangasana, Upward-Facing-Dog, Downward-Facing Dog, Lunge, Forward Bend, and Backward Bend).

https://www.stillworks.org/blog/2011/11/classic-salutations

This sequence is repeated numerous times during Vinyasa, whether the class is slow and mellow or fast and charged.

Aerial Yoga

The biggest vestibular wallop by far occurs during aerial yoga.

Aerial yoga uses a sling-like hammock suspended from the ceiling made of super stretchy, strong material. Wrapped around your body, the silky material supports your weight. As you are in the air working against gravity, the vestibular system is getting lubricated the entire time you are suspended in the hammock, the amount and intensity variable. Upside down provides the most intensity.

The benefits are numerous. In aerial yoga, you can balance more easily than on floor or mat and the support of the hammock makes difficult poses like inversions easier to get into without pressure on shoulders, head, neck or the rest of the spine. Further, the support allows you to go to your edge to improve flexibility and strength in ways you may be unable to achieve on floor or mat.

DIGGING DEEPER

While fun and invigorating, Aerial Yoga is challenging as it requires muscles and a well-developed core to manipulate your body into the postures.

The first time I took aerial yoga I thought I would hop onto the hammock, spread arms and legs and fly. Instead I spent the class prone in a fetal tuck like a baby in the hammock. At my age and handicapped by a crooked spine, I lacked strong enough arms muscles to get in and out of the poses in the air and maneuver easily in the hammock.

I never went back though I intend to. If I could develop the strength to do the practice, it's great fun and has enormous benefits.

Does your vestibular system too need oiling? To answer let's explore the many ways the vestibular system impacts functioning.

PHYSICAL

Muscle Tone & Posture

Role of Cerebellum

Do you have floppy, low muscle tone, a slouched posture, or poor coordination? If so, you might blame your vestibular system for giving faulty messaging to your brain.

The vestibular system strongly influences muscle tone and posture by telling muscles to contract to stay upright against the downward pull of gravity.

In *Balance,* Scott McCredie describes Cheryl who, following a dose of gentamicin for a post-surgery infection lost much of her balance system. When she awoke, the morning after taking the antibiotic, and tried to get up, she collapsed onto the floor and had to crawl down the stairs. As McCredie explains, "Her postural reflexes were temporarily stunned by the sudden loss of sensory input from her vestibular system" (p. 91).

I had a similar experience when I had an inner ear infection and had to lie flat for two days. I crawled up the stairs to my bedroom as I couldn't sit upright without vertigo.

In yoga, poor communication from your vestibular system and proprioceptors makes balancing a challenge and you teeter through the poses. Such instability happens particularly in postures that require much core, like inversions, as you likely have poor core muscle strength as well. Poor postural control makes even sitting up straight in Easy Pose difficult. Many with poor balance become yoga dropouts.

The vestibular system works in conjunction with the cerebellum in the old brain where messaging from the vestibular system to the brain is largely mediated.

Wrapped around the back of the brainstem, the cerebellum is the puppeteer of the nervous system, coordinating muscle tone, balance, and body movements so we move easily, smoothly, precisely and with good timing. The cerebellum appears to be also in charge of volume control for all sensory input, inhibiting or dampening sensory information so the cortex can respond better.

Head movement stimulates receptors in the vestibular apparatus. From there, neural information gets transmitted to the cerebellum and to the vestibular nuclei located in the brainstem. At the same time, sensory receptors in the muscles and joints send impulses to the cerebellum. With these proprioceptive inputs, the cerebellum, along with other parts of the brain tries to determine the location and movement of body parts.

To plan and execute movement well, messages from the vestibular and proprioceptive systems must be clear. An example of someone with the cerebellum at peak performance is Nikolas Wallenda, the first person to walk a tightrope stretched directly over *Niagara Falls*. More down to earth is Denzel Washington's classic "glide in his stride" stroll around Manhattan in *American Gangster*. "Leonine, panther like, sexy" are some of the words critics have used to describe the way Washington glides into the frame of his movies.

Clumsy people with poor coordination and stiff or flaccid rag doll muscle tone reveal a cerebellum receiving faulty vestibular and proprioceptive messages, a red flag for some problem in sensory processing. Characters like Annie Hall (Diane Keaton) and Alvy Singer (Woody Allen) in the movie *Annie Hall* come to mind. Shlumping around Manhattan, shoulders slouched, gait stiff and frantic, the two lost souls fumble awkwardly, mumbling as they struggle to make sense of things.

Faulty messaging to the cerebellum can be subtle. Recall how, though I was athletic and graceful, dance movement took concentrated effort as my body had slight, barely detectable stiffness.

So subtle was it that it eluded even Gus Giordano, the renowned jazz dance teacher who taught in Evanston Illinois and where I studied jazz dance. One day, he asked me to demonstrate to the class the routine "I'm a Brass Band" from the musical *Sweet Charity,* as he knew I loved this dance. Me! In front of all those amazing dancers, some in his dance company. I froze. With enormous effort, I marched, self-consciously, like the tin man.

Yet, with practice, practice, practice, fluidly improved. As mentioned, at age 22, I performed on PBS with his dance company in: "Michaelangelo: A Portrait in Dance."

MENTAL SHARPNESS

"Reading, writing and arithmetic... are extremely complex processes that can develop only upon a strong foundation of sensory integration."

~A. Jean Ayres

In the 1970's, A. Jean Ayres was developing the theory and therapy of sensory integration, largely to help special needs children to function better. At the heart of learning, Ayres discovered, is a well-functioning vestibular sense. The vestibular sense tells the child about "his own body and its relationship to the gravitational field of the earth, and then these become the building blocks that help him to develop the sense of sight and sound, which tell him about things that are distant from his body" wrote Ayres in *Sensory Integration and the Child* (p. 15).

In what has become a landmark study published in *Science* in 1977, a group of 26 normal infants, at around seven months of age received 16 sessions of spinning around in a chair, clockwise and counter-clockwise in a dark room. Control infants did not receive any spinning. Each spin began with a rapid acceleration, followed by one-minute of constant velocity, and ended with an abrupt halt. Four days after the spinning was over, the spun infants had reflex scores three times higher than the control groups, and motor skills more than four times better. In other words, they were smarter.

To improve learning, pediatric occupational therapists will do things like have a child swing on a swing while trying to throw a beanbag through a ring (vestibular and visual); or listen with headphones to a special programmed CD for listening therapy CD while gliding back and forth on a glider (vestibular and auditory).

In yoga, something comparable might be standing in Dancer Pose while staring at a spot on the wall (dristi).

At the same time that Ayres was developing the theory and practice of sensory integration, psychoanalyst Dr. Harold Levinson, clinical associate professor of psychiatry at New York University Medical Center was studying dyslexia. Dyslexics have a neurological disorder in the language processing system of their brain.

After examining 1,000 sufferers of dyslexia, Levinson found only 1% showed evidence of cerebral dysfunction. Seven hundred fifty of the children exhibited problems with balance and coordination. He concluded that dyslexia correlated with problems related to vestibular dysfunction, the same findings Ayres had uncovered in working with special needs children.

That vestibular functioning affects cognition makes sense. In addition to movement, the cerebellum, writes neuropsychiatrist John Ratey, author of *Spark, The Revolutionary New Science of Exercise and the Brain* "also coordinates thoughts, attention, emotions, and even social skills. . . . When we exercise, particularly if the exercise requires complex motor movements, we're also exercising the areas of the brain involved in the full suite of cognitive functions."

In other words, yoga postures that challenge balance, will improve thinking: more balanced on our feet translate to more balanced in our brains. Think of how articulate people with sharp thinking skills are described as "Thinking on their feet."

Science supports the connection between vestibular input and thinking. A study by researchers at the University of Illinois, published in 2014 in *Journal of Gerontology A* found eight weeks of Hatha yoga to improve cognitive functions of sedentary seniors. After a 20-minute yoga session, memory (particularly working memory), speed, and accuracy improved. Little wonder yoga helped the cobwebs in my brain dissipate.

In a study published in 2017, conducted at the University of Waterloo, researchers found that Hatha yoga greatly increased the energy levels of participants, further aiding focus and improving brain function. Endorphin release accounted for increased energy, as did increased blood flow from poses and breathing exercises.

Some schools incorporate chairs into the classroom that rock and swivel. Does it make a difference? Indeed. Studies show focus to improve and behavior problems to lessen. Writes Lakeside school in North Wales, Pennsylvania in their blog, "Why Rocking Chairs for Students:"

> "The motion soothes the brain and facilitates concentration along with the ability to think logically, which provides overall better cognitive processing. Rocking helps students who are experiencing a brain state of high arousal

(hypervigilance) to be able to transition to a much more calm brain state to enhance his/her ability to learn and problem-solve."

EMOTIONAL STABILITY

My neighbor Sarah shows clear signs of vestibular dysfunction—low muscle tone, clumsiness, poor balance, inability to cross the midline. For over 40 years, Sarah has been on Prozac, having suffered depression and suicidal thoughts since her teens when she attempted suicide. For anxiety, which sometimes leaves her screaming like a banshee she keeps Xanax handy.

The link between her physical and emotional state is no surprise. The vestibular system is intimately tied to mental health as physical instability causes insecurity and anxiety.

Gravitational Insecurity

Gravitational insecurity is a severe reaction to change in head position that creates fear. You might feel sudden terror with head back at the sink when getting hair washed in the salon, doing a backbend in yoga, or even leaning forward to change sheets on a bed.

Such fear happens because the slightest movement registers in the brain as "Falling!" It's most pronounced when the head tilts back, a position that creates conflicting visual information as the world appears as if turned upside down. Those with gravitational insecurity experience on-going anxiety, something I discuss in detail in *Too Loud, Too Bright.*

In yoga, the Camel Pose, an extreme backbend that stretches and opens up the whole front of the body is notorious for creating fear. Nicknamed "the fear pose," it is hyper-arousing for many and creates a scary, fluttery surge in the belly and across the chest while doing it. Some become nauseous and may even vomit.

(Jen)

Following head trauma, I was a victim of a visceral surge deep in my belly in Camel. Today, after years of yoga, along with neurocranial restructuring (NCR) for head trauma, I not only tolerate the pose, I do it comfortably with eyes shut. Apparently, years of vestibular stimulation in yoga asanas created less reactivity in my brainstem, where sensations enter, and reset my fear button.

Feeling Vulnerable

Bending backwards creates fear also because it makes you vulnerable. Our body's natural reaction to danger is to curl inward and assume a fetal tuck by rounding shoulders and upper spine, and tucking chin to chest. We do this to protect neck and chest, the most vulnerable areas of our body. Bending backwards and exposing these spaces forces us into a very vulnerable position.

If fearful, you likely hold much tension in the chest, physically and emotionally, and slump in part for protection. Animals will curl up in self-protection. When they open up, like my cat Pumpkin—belly up on the floor, legs spread, begging for stroking—it signals how safe he feels. B.K.S. Iyengar encouraged depressed people to go for poses that keep armpits open.

Our sedentary lifestyle encourages a slumped posture, contributing to a fearful mindset. We spend our day forward: forward brushing our teethe; forward over a desk; forward staring at a screen; forward driving; forward dining.

Yoga gets our bodies *up*.

Stress Response

We've talked a bit about how yoga asanas reduces the stress response. To get more technical, sensory input into the postures inhibits the HPA axis, our central stress response. The HPA axis represents the interaction of the hypothalamus, the pituitary and the adrenal glands.

Located within the emotional limbic system, the hypothalamus, the "master gland" controls visceral processes: body temperature, hunger, thirst, fatigue, sleep and circadian rhythms. When we feel a threat, the amygdala triggers the hypothalamus to activate the sympathetic nervous system into flight/fight. This sets up a chain reaction of hormonal release from the pituitary, causing the adrenals to pump out cortisol.

The vestibular system is a key player in inhibiting the HPA axis and reducing stress because it weaves throughout the hypothalamus, as well as the amygdala. All that vestibular input during yoga practice inhibits the posterior (sympathetic area) of the hypothalamus, diminishing the stress response and turning on the parasympathetic calming mode. At the same time, the breath and the focus on the present stop the brain from automatically invoking the stress response.

The vestibular system weaves as well through the hippocampus. The part of the limbic system responsible for memory, learning and stress reduction, the hippocampus has high cortisol receptors and powerfully connects to the HPA axis. That's why we forget things when stressed.

Severe stress damages the hippocampus and reduces new neuron production. This explains why thinking and memory suffers when depressed, abused, or suffering PTSD. During recovery from depression and stress, the production of new brain cells in the hippocampus increases.

Chill Neurotransmitter

The magic potion behind inhibition of the HPA axis is GABA (gamma-Aminobutyric acid), our chill neurotransmitter. Vestibular stimulation increases the release of GABA hugely.

How important is this for reducing stress? Very. GABA acts as a check-and-balance system in the brain, lowering the volume on overall neuron activity and restraining excitement in the brain to operate at a steady pace. In other words, vestibular input during yoga practice modulates excitability in large part by releasing GABA, producing that yoga wave of calmness of body and stillness of mind.

When GABA is deficient, emotions and anxiety run wild and you have difficulty handling stress. Drugs that increase GABA activity, like benzodiazepines (Xanax for instance) are commonly prescribed to improve mood and decrease anxiety. I take GABA directly as a dietary supplement for a restful nightly sleep.

Sense of Self

By affecting emotions, the vestibular system impacts sense of self. If you are grounded and balanced while walking the earth, you feel grounded and balanced in life. If you are ungrounded and wobbly, you feel emotionally "off balance," and suffer poor mental health.

Such physical instability can erupt into anxiety disorders, including space related phobias like fear of heights, fear of flying, claustrophobia and panic attack. In fact, panic attack and vestibular dysfunction share the same symptoms: dizziness, disorientation, lightheadedness, floating, faintness, nausea.

Instability can also result in depression. "Depression," says psychologist and yogic scholar Richard Miller, "is the feeling of separation from self."

INTERESTING INFO

DOUBLE-JOINTEDNESS & PANIC ATTACK

Those with "hypermobility syndrome" or double jointedness, an inherited trait, commonly experience panic attacks. Apparently, they appear to inherit a fear gene. At the same time, people with hyper-mobility syndrome have wobbly ankles and feet and therefore poor balance. Their panic may be set off by this instability, in other words by vestibular dysfunction, as well as a faulty gene sequence.

Information regarding movement transmits to areas of the brain such as the temporo-parietal junction (TPJ). The TPJ plays a crucial role in distinguishing self from others, and in understanding your beliefs, desires, and emotions, as well as those of others. Damage to this area has produced out-of-body experiences, as awareness becomes skewed.

Studies confirm the link between vestibular disorders and depersonalization and de-realization symptoms. These symptoms include feeling "spaced out," "body feeling strange" and "not feeling in control of self." The same symptoms are described during panic attack, a condition typified by disembodiment. Feeling greatly threatened, the system goes into freeze—plays dead. The parasympathetic nervous system is dominant and the whole body shuts down.

This was Nadia's experience. Head trauma from a car accident resulted in TMJ and Meniere's disease, an ear disorder that causes dizziness, ringing and pressure build up. Since then, she has had out-of-body experiences. Before reading an early draft of this book, she assumed they were psychological and didn't connect them with her vestibular issues. An avid yogi, Nadia has found yoga to reduce stress and dizziness.

Throughout history, vestibular stimulation has been used to treat mental health issues. In the nineteenth century, mania or elevated arousal was treated with a spinning chair. Today, electrodes are placed in the brain to create vestibular stimulation and alleviate depression, anxiety, and stress.

A study done at the University of Rochester in the late 1990's on nursing home patients found that in those who rocked in a rocking chair more than 80 minutes a day, behaviors such as crying, tension, anxiety and depressed mood dropped. The heavy rockers also requested less pain medication.

HEARING

As the vestibular sense resides in the inner ear, hearing is intimately tied to vestibular functioning. If you suffer auditory processing issues, a faulty vestibular system is at fault.

I'm one who does. Following more than a few of a yoga teacher's instructions is nary impossible for me, short of exhaustively using every neuron in my brain to process the words.

Take a pose like Half Lord of the Fishes B. Though I know the pose once I see it, I don't know it by name but must follow the teacher's instructions:

"Sit in Easy Pose. Extend right leg, cross the left leg over the right and place the left foot flat on the floor close to the right knee. Bend the right leg to bring the right heel next to the left hip. Wrap the right hand around the left knee and pull the knee in towards your chest..."

What a mouthful. I can't follow more than two directions in a sequence, let alone a dozen. I glance around to see what others are doing. Hmm, some others too look confused, while some have twisted to their left.

Many people have difficulty following a long sequence of directions. Recently in Iyengar, Stephanie was demonstrating a variation of reclined pigeon where you bend your knees, cross one ankle over the other knee, clasp hands around knee and pull knee and foot toward you. In this variation, the elbow wrapped around the knee and the leg pulled back toward the head, while the other leg extended straight forward in the air. After demonstrating, Stephanie talked us through the pose. Half the class had it wrong. "Hmmm," said Stephanie looking around miffed, "and I both demonstrated and talked you through it."

Another one of my teachers, when many can't quite get it, will say to the class, "You're not listening."

Of course neither myself, nor the others are not "listening." We're not *processing*, as our brains take longer to make sense of auditory information. To follow the practice, I must SEE the pose, as well as HEAR the instructions. Fortunately, in more basic classes the teacher does the pose with you to demonstrate.

VISION

If you've ever taken ballet, you know that to do a pirouette you must keep your eyes dead on a spot straight ahead for as long as possible, before whipping your head around and completing the turn. If not, you'll get thrown off balance.

In yoga practice, dristi, or focusing on a spot is encouraged in poses to keep you focused, present, concentrating, and, in balancing poses to keep you stay steady on feet.

When you move your head and eyes together to look up or down, or side to side both the visual and vestibular systems join forces to convey to the brain a visual map. This map enables you to know where you are in space, integrating the visual and vestibular.

In fact, ninety percent of the cells in the visual cortex respond to vestibular stimulation. Picture how the vestibular system guides the movement of your eyes, enabling you to track moving cars. If your head turns to the right, your eyes will typically follow and settle on a target giving your brain a reference point for the balance system. When we move our head and eyes together, to look up or down, both the visual and vestibular systems work in tandem to give the brain a clear message about body position.

If your vestibular system needs oiling, tramping down a dimly lit staircase without vision to rely on, or, in yoga, balancing in a class with dim light proves difficult.

Does yoga improve vision?

Several studies have shown that it can.

A 1995 study reported that after 10 days of yoga training, a group of college students had improved visual discrimination and were better able to focus and process visual information.

A 2004, Indian, study compared the performance scores of children (aged 11 to 16 years) in verbal and spatial memory tests for two groups, one attending a yoga camp and the other a fine arts camp. The yoga group showed 43% increase in spatial memory scores, while the fine arts and control groups showed no change.

Chewing gum during yoga practice also helps vestibular function and vision. Yep. Chewing gum is neither rude nor silly. It does wonders for eyes, for posture, and for calming.

Chewing gum boosts activity in the frontal lobe of the brain, making you more alert and able to concentrate by focusing your eyes. To demonstrate, look at these words. Now chomp down. Notice how your eyes focus when you bite down. The harder the gum, the more effort it takes to chew and the greater the effect.

Chewing gum has more benefits. The jaw is one of the main joints in our body and chewing gum applies proprioceptive input that releases feel good neurotransmitters, decreasing cortisol and reducing stress and drowsiness. This is why we eat when stressed.

Chewing gum also improves posture. In a 2011 the study, "Effect of chewing gum on static posturography in patients with balance disorders," published in Acata Otolarngology, researchers found posture to improve while chewing gum. The researchers concluded that chewing gum indirectly affected postural control by influencing vestibular function to stabilize posture during upright standing.

Occupational therapists use gum chewing for children as a tool to reduce anxiety and increase focus. They even write it into the child's school IEP.

Gauging Distance

Another problem you might experience with poor visual processing is gauging distance. My visual-spatial processing issues exacerbated following head trauma, in large part from trauma to my right eye, and my two eyes were not working together. Slowly, visual processing problems intensified and I no longer perceived my body in space clearly.

Unable to gauge distance well, driving was a challenge, especially because I was so spacey. I backed into a tree and smashed one side of my car. I backed into a garbage can and smashed the other side of my car. All my hubcaps had all fallen off from so many sideswipes. Within a period of two months I had hit four cars and lost my driver's license for a year. Fortunately no one was hurt. My car was all smashed up and had to be junked for the parts.

In yoga, gauging distance is important in a crowded class to give those around you enough space so arms and legs don't intertwine. On the fourth of July the morning class was packed like sardines. The only way to avoid getting whacked was to move my body *very* consciously. While I managed to not knock anyone, I got sideswiped twice, once by a young gal to the left of me and again from a little kick against my extended leg from a middle-aged woman in front of me.

Neither may have necessarily *had* problems gauging distance. Still, sensory processing disorder can be mild and subtle and some in the class might. At least a few though likely confused right from left.

Confusing Left from Right

I'm lying on the floor in Anuttara Raja. Philip says "Extend your right leg" and I do. Several others have extended their left leg. Philip jokes, "The right leg is the one on the right side of your body."

Not differentiating right from left is common in yoga, even in advanced classes. Judy, after having the class do a pose on the right side of the body will joke, "Now do the other right side" as so many have done the pose on the left side first. So common is the problem of not knowing left from right that a study of college-age students showed 26% still struggled to some degree with the concept.

The ability to learn left and right isn't well understood. But it likely relates to how the brain makes sense of where objects are in space. This includes one's own body parts, in other words body awareness relates to having good visual-spatial processing.

Let's now explore how joints and muscles work with your sense of balance to give you your "place in space."

RECAP

VESTIBULAR SYSTEM:

- Controls sense of balance (gyroscope), orientation (compass), and movement against gravity.

- Information from inner ear gives feedback of our head's position: upright, tilted, flexed, extended or rotated. Every time we move up or down, side to side, back and forth or in a circle we tap into the vestibular sense.

- Unifying system for all sensory input, impacting how we move through space to how we think and how we feel.
    - regulates muscle tone, motor control, and postural control;
    - sequencing of movement, visual space perception, and visual-motor control;
    - auditory language skills, emotional stability, clear thinking and alertness.

WHEN ON SHAKY GROUND

Physical Consequences:

- dizziness, nausea, adrenal overload, low muscle tone, tension, pain, or many other symptoms.

- loss of balance and falling easily;

- dizziness when moving in ways that challenge the vestibular system, like tilting the head backward or moving backward;

- crippling vertigo, especially those that suffer Meniere's disease.

Emotional:

- get frustrated easily and hate being inside body;

- depression, anger, fear, or hostility.

Mental:

- confusion, disorganization, spaciness, and poor memory;

- space related phobias, like fear of and heights

- disassociation

A Shaky World. Estimates are that vestibular disorders occur in more than 35% of adults aged 40 or older in the US. Injury, disease, certain drugs, even the aging process itself, can put us on shaky ground.

> **Low End.** Love adrenaline rush of fast cars, motor boats, roller coasters, flying; getting body pummeled, as when white water rafting; and defying gravity, like diving from the high board. On the mat, you love defying gravity with lots of inversions and may enjoy Kundalini yoga with all the side-to-side, back and forth and up and down rocking and swaying.

> **High End.** Become quickly overloaded by vestibular input as the vestibular system tries to process too many sensations at once; get easily car sick, sea sick and avoid roller coasters at all costs. In yoga, you might become

dizzy when the head is tilted back, as in backbends, and get anxious doing the Camel.

YOGA & VESTIBULAR INPUT

- Many yoga asanas force you to lift your body against gravity, such as Boat, Bow, Bridge, Cobra, and Wheel.

- Frequent head change occurs as you go from horizontal to vertical to angular planes while moving in and out of upright, inverted, prone, supine or sidelying positions.

VESTIBULAR & PHYSICAL FUNCTIONING

Muscle Tone & Posture. Vestibular system strongly influences muscle tone and posture by telling muscles to contract to stay upright against the downward pull of gravity. In yoga, poor communication from your vestibular system and proprioceptors makes balancing a challenge and you teeter through the poses.

Role of Cerebellum. To plan and execute movement well, messages from the vestibular and proprioceptive systems must be clear. Clumsy people with poor coordination and stiff or flaccid rag doll muscle tone reveal a cerebellum receiving faulty vestibular and proprioceptive messages, a red flag for some problem in sensory processing.

MENTAL SHARPNESS. At the heart of learning is a well-functioning vestibular sense.

EMOTIONAL STABILITY. Vestibular system is intimately tied to mental health as physical instability causes insecurity and anxiety.

Gravitational Insecurity. A severe reaction to change in head position that creates fear; most pronounced when the head tilts back like in Camel Pose in yoga.

Stress Response. Sensory input into postures inhibits the HPA axis, our central stress response. Vestibular system a key player in inhibiting the HPA axis and reducing stress because it weaves throughout the hypothalamus, as well as the amygdala.

Chill Neurotransmitter. Behind inhibition of the HPA axis is GABA (gamma-Aminobutyric acid), our chill neurotransmitter. Vestibular stimulation increases the release of GABA hugely.

Sense of Self. By affecting emotions, the vestibular system impacts sense of self. If you are grounded and balanced walking the earth, you feel grounded and balanced in life. If you are ungrounded and wobbly, you feel emotionally "off balance," and suffer poor mental health.

HEARING. As the vestibular sense resides in the inner ear, hearing is intimately tied to vestibular functioning. If you suffer auditory processing issues, a faulty vestibular system is at fault. Following more than a few of a yoga teacher's instructions is a challenge.

VISION. When you move your head and eyes together to look up or down, or side to side both the visual and vestibular systems join forces to convey to the brain a visual map. This map enables you to know where you are in space, integrating the visual and vestibular.

Gauging Distance. Might experience problem with gauging distance if you have poor visual processing. In yoga, gauging distance is important in a crowded class to give those around you enough space so arms and legs don't intertwine.

Confusing Left from Right. Not differentiating right from left is common in yoga, even in advanced classes.

CHAPTER 5

PROPRIOCEPTION: PLACE IN SPACE

"Sense of place is the sixth sense, an internal compass and map made by memory and spatial perception together."

~ REBECCA SOLNIT

The other day in Iyenger class, it was time to do Bow Pose. The teacher told us to lie on our bellies on our mats, bend our knees while keeping our feet hip-width apart, raise our legs, and grab our ankles from the outside.

Something felt strange. I was miffed. What was the problem? I couldn't figure it out.

The teacher came over, "Sharon, grab your right foot on the outside, not the inside." Ahhh. While I had grabbed my left foot on the outside, I had the wrong grip on the right leg. *What was wrong with me?*

Eventually I figured out the confusion. In Anuttara Raja, the teachers tell us to grab our ankles from the *inside* when doing Bow Pose, not the outside. My brain had combined the two holds.

Still, why couldn't I figure out why the position felt wrong? Why was I having such a poor *proprioception* day?

Proprioception is our second *power* sense. Located in our joints, muscles, tendons and ligaments, proprioceptive receptors give us our sense of body position and body awareness. It works like this. Information comes from our eyes, and receptors in our skin, muscles, and joints that sense stretch, pressure, and movement. The brain processes the sensory input to give us a "mind's eye" view of how our body parts are positioned and moving through three-dimensional space.

This information enables us to move, plan and make adjustments (coordinate movements) without using vision. It allows us to walk with a steady stride; to bring our wine glass to our lips and sip; to be aware of lifting our legs and chest at the same time and level in Bow Pose.

(Jen)

Oh yes, and to recognize in Bow when you have the wrong grip!

The sobriety test of stretching your arm out to the side, closing your eyes, and touching your finger to your nose is a proprioceptive test.

To get a sense of proprioception, close your eyes and bring your index fingers together to touch in front of your nose. In milliseconds, proprioceptor cells in the fingertips fired off to chat with your brain to enable you to do this.

Proprioception even works when asleep, making us aware of our position so we don't fall out of bed. If you have poor proprioception, you might fall out of bed even as an adult. This happened several times to a friend of mine who has floppy muscle tone, which equates with poor proprioception.

GRAND MODULATOR

My friend Kristin was jumpy and couldn't sit still. "I'm so stressed," she said. She reached into her purse for a Xanax pill.

"Wait," I said. "Try this first."

I positioned her into Tug-of-War: facing each other, arms outstretched toward the other and hands pushed into the other's palms, feet forcefully pressed into the ground. "Now, push as hard as you can until you feel exhausted."

She did, her face turning red, and didn't let go for a few minutes.

"How do you feel now?"

"Much calmer."

"Do you still need your Xanax?"

She laughed. "Not at the moment."

By pushing hard into each other, we both got a quick spurt of "heavy work," hefty extension and flexion of the joints and muscular exertion.

The proprioceptive system is the grand modulator of the nervous system, getting us quickly into that "just right place," as A. Jean Ayres termed it. If you feel hyper and jumpy, it calms you; if you feel lethargic and bored, it revs you up.

It does so because proprioception elicits a perfectly balanced chemical cocktail.

Chemical Balance

Proprioceptive input releases serotonin and dopamine. Serotonin and dopamine wash away cortisol and adrenaline, involved in the fight/flight response of the sympathetic nervous system.

Serotonin though does much more. The master regulating chemical in the cortex, serotonin sets the firing level for all other neurotransmitters to keep moods stable.

Dopamine

Of particular importance is serotonin's role in releasing dopamine in the right amount.

Dopamine motivates us to seek reward and pleasure. When the brain is charged with dopamine, we are on top of the world: sex feels great; food is scrumptious; yoga is at the height of pleasure.

When dopamine is too much or too little you become unstable. Too much dopamine leads to hyperactivity or aggression, while too little leads to poor motivation and enthusiasm. Even worse, too little can result in fatigue, depression, stress, poor concentration and memory, and you fail to complete tasks or work toward goals. To charge the system and boost dopamine, many will engage in risk taking and addictive behavior.

Having sufficient serotonin in our brain ensures that we go to neither extreme.

Norepinephrine

When serotonin drops, as it does when depressed, it impacts the level of another neurotransmitter: norepinephrine. Norepinephrine is needed for arousal. Not having enough makes you less alert and lowers energy—both symptoms associated with depression.

Boosting Serotonin

If you boost serotonin, as you do from the massive proprioceptive input in yoga practice, you keep your system in a balanced state. Writes John Ratey in *Spark, The Revolutionary New Science of Exercise and the Brain,* a widely popular best seller, "I tell people that going for a run is a little bit like taking Prozac and a little bit like taking Ritalin because, like the drugs, exercise elevates these neurotransmitters.... A deeper explanation is that exercise *balances* these neurotransmitters."

Usually, familiar, repetitive activities boost serotonin levels in the brain, lowering arousal level, while novel or non-rhythmic activities boost dopamine to perk you up. With the exception of Bikram and Ashtanga, which repeat the same poses, most yoga classes offer both: familiar, repeated poses for a serotonin shot; varying, unexpected sequences for a dopamine shot.

Even pushing yourself to go to class when too tired, too pre-occupied, or too depressed will increase dopamine. This is because taking steps toward reaching your goals stimulates dopamine levels.

Flying High

You know that feeling in yoga when you're flying high and the world feels great. Intuitively, it might seem the euphoria comes from the release of endorphins, the brain's opiate (discussed in detail on the next page). In fact, it might be from the release of serotonin.

Released in large amounts, serotonin produces a rush that translates into an emotional high. A strenuous class like power Vinyasa gives you more than 20 minutes of intense heavy work from challenging poses, including balancing on one leg, hand balancing, and inversions. These poses give you a massive serotonin pow.

(James)

The bigger the joint the greater is the release of serotonin. The hips are the biggest joint making poses that strongly engage the hips especially calming. This explains why the Garland, an intense squat at the onset of my Anuttara Raja yoga class launches me quickly into a relaxed state.

The large amount of serotonin released in Vinyasa explains the sudden rush I feel halfway through the flow, when *everything's right in the world*. I don't feel the same rush halfway through Iyengar, Kundalini or Anuttara Raja. While there's huge muscular engagement in Iyengar, there's a lot of time between poses as the teacher explains the next pose and you set up the needed props. Kundalini poses involve less muscular engagement than Vinyasa, while Anuttara Raja encourages muscular dis-engagement.

In her 2017 interview with *Yoga Journal*, Elizabeth Gilbert also describes that magic halfway point during Vinyasa, albeit differently than my experience. "There always comes that one holy moment, usually somewhere in the middle of the class, when I suddenly find that I have shed my pain and failings, that I have shed my heavy human mind, and that I have metamorphosed for just an instant into something else: an eagle, a cat, a crane, a dolphin, a child."

The more strenuous the class, the longer the after-class buzz. For me, that's around two hours following Power Vinyasa yoga.

Endorphins

Along with releasing serotonin, yoga practice stimulates the pituitary (third eye) gland to release endorphins.

Acting as a communication channel between the brain and nervous system, endorphins replace fear, anxiety and worry with a sense of euphoria—the "runner's high." Its primary purpose though is to relieve pain. This is why, under stress, people will be unaware of an injury until the stress is over. This had an evolutionary advantage. In ancient times, one could ignore pain and continue to run from the tiger.

The so-called euphoria of the "runner's high" reportedly takes an hour of running or strenuous physical activity. In other words, it takes great effort to achieve it. Once you do though it's addictive and gets runners on the track, day after day, rain or shine.

Can yoga give you the same euphoria? It can but only in more advanced classes that offer considerable heavy work throughout, from challenging inversions, and arm and leg balances.

Who needs booze, coke, or Prozac!

HOW YOGA CREATES SPACE

From the repetitive flow of postures, to the changing body positions while flowing through the poses, to the compression of muscles and joints in bends, twists, turns and balancing poses yoga asanas provide a proprioceptive cornucopia.

They do so by providing repeated and extremes of pushing (extension) and pulling (flexion)—heavy work. Isometric postures *pull*, like Upward-Facing-Dog, Bow pose, Dancer pose, Pigeon, and seated forward folds, while poses that challenge balance, like weight bearing one legged or arm balancing poses and inversions, *push*.

In balance postures and in inversions, your own body weight is pushed into the ground. Challenging to do, (whoever said yoga was a simple stretch class!) weight bearing poses force you to use muscles against gravity. Poses like Dancer strongly engage the proprioceptors with much input into the ankles, knees, hip flexors, wrists and shoulders. Additionally, it requires significant strength to remain grounded as you extend your arm and leg outward.

While balancing on one leg places deep pressure into the bottom of the foot, balancing on arms places deep pressure into the palms. With all this input, imagine the calming rush in a pose like firefly!

(Marissa)

As an added bonus, weight bearing poses help movements to become more and more coordinated and smooth, and bones, joints, and muscles to become stronger and increasingly stable. This makes weight bearing poses especially helpful for those with low muscle tone.

All this input makes yoga practice a proprioceptive feast. And this massive input translates off the mat as exercises that heighten proprioceptive awareness allow the body to become more efficient in everyday movement.

A Milder Buzz

Relatively easy poses too can involve much pushing and pulling into the joints and muscles for heavy work.

An example is the Triangle.

Triangle creates rich proprioception because it's about

(Marjorie)

stretching and extending—as long as you do it correctly. I did it wrong for years as my tensed up shoulders prevented me from fully extending my torso. Tense shoulders don't work in yoga. *Tension* doesn't work in yoga because it constricts muscles, preventing strong proprioception.

One day Judy corrected me. "Extend your torso," she said, as she gently extended my arm up. I did and Judy gave me her classic approval: "Ahhh."

From then on, I saw the pose as creating space. Now, I lean, lean, lean gracefully to my right side, my arm out wide and, feeling like a marionette on a string being pulled by the puppeteer, lower my arm down slowly and rest the back of my hand carefully on my lower leg. Boom! My whole body seems to fall into place.

Proprioception and Muscle *Dis*-Engagement

Created by Philip Christodoulou, Anuttara Raja is focused on stretching fascia, the connective tissue that attaches muscles. You do so mostly by lying on the floor in challenging configurations as you mold, push, shape, and tug to get into the twist, the bend, and other formations.

You stay in these contorted poses for 3-5 minutes to move from superficial fascia to deep fascia, connective tissue made up of collagen. This action allows joints and fascia to release and relax, boosting the presence of alpha waves in the brain and reducing stress and anxiety.

To get to know the web that holds you together, you need to relax your muscles during Raja and let gravity take over. "In Anuttara Raja we worship a higher force—gravity," quips Philip.

In other words, your goal during class is muscle disengagement. Yet, you still get much proprioceptive input.

CLARIFYING

While Anuttara yoga is similar to yin yoga, in that they both hold poses to release fascia, the two have distinct differences. While yin emphasizes the physical practice, Anuttara emphasizes more the spiritual practice. Also, yin practice keeps the room cool to best release fascia, while Anuttara Raja believes heat keeps the muscles relaxed and the room temperature is around 93.°

Easy Pose (cross-legged position) begins the Anuttara Raja class, providing input into hips, ankles and knees. Next is Child Pose, along with a twist to both sides in the pose. Easy enough.

Yet in addition to flexion in the hips and knees, strong pull into the shoulder provides the heavy work for rich proprioception.

From Child, you move into two intense poses.

"Toe Cruncher" pushes heavily into the toe joints for intense heavy work—thus the name Toe Cruncher—as well as providing input into the ankles, hips and knees. You stay in Toe Cruncher for an agonizing couple of minutes as you do a few breathing exercises, and then twist to both sides.

(Jen)

Though uncomfortable and challenging for most, Toe Cruncher has great benefits. Kneeling with the toes tucked under lengthens the plantar muscles on the sole of the foot. This helps with plantar fasciitis, a condition in which the muscles become inflamed, something I've suffered for years. Toe Crunch is also a great pose to stretch the arch or the sole of the foot, improving flexibility and loosening tension.

With my lousy feet, sorely out of alignment from my back issues, the pose is excruciating. Still, I persist until the teacher says that magic word, "Release." Such persistence strengthens my resolve off the mat. "I can do it. I can ride it out."

The next pose is the Garland—the "Royal Diamond."

(Jen)

Notice all the deep flexion into the ankles, knees, hip flexors, as well as flexion into wrists, elbows and shoulders. It especially heavily engages the hip proprioceptors and, unless you reside in a village in India where you've squatted your whole life, the pose challenges all but the super flexible. Advanced yogis in my Vinyasa class squat and converse. Amazes me.

As you can see, from the get-go you've received a proprioceptive wallop even in a class that *avoids muscle engagement.*

Proprioceptive input is buttressed by some vestibular input and deep pressure tactile input from lying pushed into the hard floor, even without engaging muscle. Add three to four calming breathing exercises, soothing heat, comforting darkness, and the ambient peaceful sounds of Deva Premal singing in Sanskrit, and I feel wrapped in a sensory cocoon.

LOCATION OF PROPRIOCEPTORS

Proprioceptors are located throughout the body. Major clusters though reside at the soles of our feet, ankles, hips, spine (to help with spinal stability), and neck.

Particularly important are the proprioceptors in the neck and ankles, both significant for yoga practice.

Neck

You have a lot of proprioceptors in your neck because your brain wants to know the position of your head at all times. The positioning of your head will directly influence the way your body moves.

In Vinyasa yoga, the head position keeps changing. By sensing the direction the head is turned, the neck sensors aid the vestibular system with head positioning. This is why it's difficult to move your head in balance poses like Ardha Chandrasana (Half Moon).

(Jen)

Ankles

Sensory feedback from the ankles tells the brain the body's movement relative to the ground to help maintain balance. The ankles also sense weight changes and motion that occur when you change positions, such as moving from one yoga pose to another.

Feet

If anyone wears socks during yoga, you know they're a greenhorn. Yoga classes are practiced barefoot, enhancing deep pressure to the bottom of the foot.

Sensors in the feet enable you discriminate the quality of that surface (hard, soft, bumpy, flat, slippery, uneven, etc.) and to sense your alignment by feeling increase or decrease in pressure in contact with the floor. This pressure tells you where your center of gravity is in relation to your foundation. Better muscle control stabilizes feet, hands or whatever other part of the body serves as your foundation in contact with the floor, leading to better balance.

In turn, greater stability within your body makes it easier to control your muscles, while improved muscle strength means also improved proprioception, yielding better control of movement and balance.

Over time, being barefoot translates into running, walking, and even standing with better posture, more mobility, a stronger body, less joint pain and a better yoga practice.

There's more good news. Studies show that stimulating the nerve endings on the bottom of the feet can decrease blood pressure and reduce sympathetic activity, reducing stress and inflammation.

Before starting class, you can work the feet by standing on a tennis ball and rolling it back and forth under your foot. This works the toes, the ball of the foot, the arch, and the heel.

Yoga Foot

"Damn yoga," Tanya (Christine Baranski) says in the movie *Mama Mia*, as she struggles to put on boots. This is because her feet have likely widened.

During class, look around you and notice the width between toes. If one is a dedicated yogi, toes may be splayed out like a Chinese fan. This will come from years of yoga teachers telling you to spread your toes to widen the feet. Doing so creates a stable base for proper alignment.

Yogis describe the foot as the foundation of the temple of the body. To support the structure above—legs, spine, arms, and head—the feet must be balanced and sturdy. A tilted or collapsed base will reflect up through the body as distortion or misalignment. "Yoga foot" increases sensory feedback to the CNS (brain and spine), improving the stability of the body in the upright position to help you know your center of gravity—to know that your foundation and the earth's center are all in one line.

This stability comes not only from spreading toes but paying attention to the arch of your foot in a pose. If you put your weight on the inner edge of your foot, your legs tend to bow inward; on the outer edge, the knees tend to bow out.

"Lift your inner arch," James tells the class, standing in Wide-Legged Forward Bend. I do and my body stabilizes.

Standing poses are the primary tools for building stability in the feet to support proper posture. Balance poses, when the proprioceptive system is particularly challenged, require working consciously with the yoga foot to heighten sensory feedback from the body and stabilize the body.

If you have contorted feet, as I do, because my body is so off balance, you can help correct this by wearing toe spacers that create space between toes to help you stand with stability. I wear *Correct Toes* during practice. According to their website, *Correct Toes* are "Proven to improve balance and proprioception in yoga." This I've experienced, and it has extended beyond my practice.

For years, I had been unable to walk barefoot as doing so would create instant discomfort. After two months of wearing *Correct Toes* in yoga and at home, my feet are more balanced and I am now walking barefoot on my ceramic floors with less pain or discomfort.

PSYCHOLOGICAL SENSE OF SPACE

Some people have great proprioception and move purposefully, gracefully, rhythmically. Good body awareness grounds you and you feel well connected to the body you inhabit.

When you are able to feel your edges, you know where your body ends and the world begins. This enables you to be aware of the boundaries of the space your body occupies without losing self. Comfortable within space, you move through the world as if embedded in it. This strong sense of physical self gives you emotional security and confidence and lays the foundation for and is crucial to psychological self-awareness.

In yoga, you tune into space and how your body occupies that space. You do so by paying attention to the sensations your body is feeling; through awareness of the music playing and your teacher's low, lilting voice; by feeling strong hands pushing your body into the correct stance; through perception of your mat in a sea of other mats.

Poor Proprioception

Some people have poor proprioception. Slumped, you shlep as if trekking through mud, muscles weak and limp. Lacking good body awareness, you don't experience living in three dimensions. "I don't want to be inside this body!" your inner voice yells.

Such discomfort enacts a huge psychological price. Feeling confused about your place in space makes discerning your personal boundaries tricky and you lack an inner compass.

The result is a body and brain fixed on keeping the self together. That leaves you stuck in survival and protection mode in the brainstem, as basic subcortical needs must be met before higher learning may take place in the cerebral cortex. As a result:

you may not think logically or rationally; you may be attention seeking, and act silly, loud and clingy; you may get too "up close and personal," invading the other's space to find your edges; in yoga you may sit too close to another's mat.

As you feel and look awkward, body image suffers as well. In some cases, poor body awareness leads to extreme disturbances to body image, as happens with eating disorders like bulimia and anorexia nervosa, out-of-body experiences, and phantom limb phenomenon.

With anorexia nervosa, for instance, the person will look in the mirror and see a distorted representation of body as being larger than it actually is, making one look fat. In out-of-body experiences, the person feels separate from her body, and her body not under her control. In the phantom limb phenomenon, the person perceives the amputated limb to exist.

Hypotonia

People who feel most physically ungrounded are those with low, fleshy muscle tone, called hypotonia. Those with this condition can't fight gravity and tend to slouch, lean and shuffle.

You do great in yoga though and are naturally drawn to it as your body is loose, making it flexible. At the same time, however, such looseness makes it hard to feel muscles activate easily. For instance, you might not have a clue as to how to tighten your stomach muscles and use core, and your midsection may feel loose.

While everyone's in awe of how you contort your body into poses only babies are supposed to be able to do, you can't feel your body as you do it and you flop into a pose like a rag doll.

Poor coordination and muscle weakness stem from hypotonia and it takes nine times the effort to get enough activation and generate enough information for the muscles and joint receptors to register. This means you must put in much more effort than others to build muscle.

Residing on shaky ground, you may avoid exercise altogether. All journeys start with the first step. If that step is shaky, you're not motivated to take the second one.

What's more, hypotonic people are more at risk of bending their joints the wrong way as hypermobility regularly accompanies hypotonia. Hypermobility means you hyper extend your joints past the traditional range of motion of other people and you are more susceptible to injury. While joints have extreme range of motion, the muscles don't allow for as much movement. This makes you vulnerable to serious injury when, in yoga you go further in stretches, bends, twists and turns than you have muscles to sustain.

My yoga teacher Judy knows well the pain from hypermobility. While another yoga teacher adjusted her ankle in a pose, Judy's ankle snapped, though the teacher had employed little pressure. For weeks, she hobbled on crutches.

"Be happy if you're blessed with stiffness," Judy will say in class.

Yoga Wakes Up the Muscles

Moving through asanas increases muscle tone and "wakes up" the muscles to decrease hypotonia. This happens because muscle activation is what gives you proprioception and the primary way you feel your body.

Increased muscle tone updates the map of your body. You feel more embodied and grounded and better about being inside your body. This feeling of being grounded comes from alpha waves stabilizing and comforting us.

Science backs up how yoga creates a new body map. Using MRI scans, a fascinating study in 2014 by Chantal Villemure and Catherine Bushnell of the National Center for Complementary and Alternative Medicine in Bethesda, Md. revealed yoga practitioners to have more brain cells. The more hours practiced a week, the larger the brain volume in the somatosensory cortex, which contains a mental map of our body; the superior parietal cortex, involved in directing attention; the hippocampus, helping yogis dampen stress; the visual cortex; and the precuneus and the posterior cingulate cortex. All are areas key to self-conceptualization.

A slow intense warrior series in a basic Vinyasa class is great to increase muscle tone. Even better are yoga practices like Iyengar and Bikram, as you hold poses longer and this builds strength and muscle tone. In Iyengar practice poses are held for long periods and modified with props such as belts, blocks, and blankets. These props aid in performing asanas correctly to minimize risk of injury or strain, and to make the postures accessible to both young and old.

Stiff and Ungrounded

One day Judy said to me, "I have students with firm muscles who don't feel grounded. Why would that be?"

If you have firm muscle tone, it would follow logically that you should have good proprioception and therefore good body awareness. But behavior is never straight forward and I'm a prime example.

One of the activities Patti Oetter had me do while at the Ayres clinic in California was to listen to "Sacred Earth Drums" by David and Steve Gordon while gliding on a large glider.

"Where are you feeling the drums?" Patti asked.

"In my head."

"Anywhere else?

"Not really."

"You're all in your head," she said. Apparently, the drumbeat should have reverberated throughout my body. My extreme spaciness, along with minor problems with bilateral integration and praxis, as well as weakened muscles threw me into la la land, though my body is firm.

AGE & PROPRIOCEPTION

As we grow older, proprioception deteriorates and causes joints to deteriorate: knowing the specific position of our joints, particularly the knee and ankle joint, and whether they are properly aligned, becomes harder. Abnormal joint biomechanics during normal daily activities like walking and arthritis often result.

Balance too becomes harder. To balance, the visual, vestibular and proprioceptive senses gather information from our bodies and surrounding environment, and send it to the brain where it's processed. Our brain sends signals back to the muscles to make necessary adjustments in position, contraction or relaxation. With loss of proprioception, this process is interrupted.

To no surprise, regular yoga practice improves balance to keep you young. As the brain changes in response to repeated stimuli, repeated positioning of body and joints in specific positions increases cortical representation of the joints, enhancing joint proprioception.

As a senior, I can attest to this. While balancing is more difficult than when I was younger, I can still stand easily enough on one leg and balance in Tree Pose. Every time I do, a smile spreads across my face. Most my age would be wobbling all over the place.

Yoga's ability to improve balance during asanas translates off the mat as heightened proprioception allows the body to become more efficient in everyday movement.

So found a 2018 study from Australia, published in *Public Health Research & Practice* that evaluated the feasibility and effectiveness of a group-based yoga program for people aged 60 and over. The object of the study was to determine if yoga prevents falls among older people.

While one-half of the participants participated in a twice-weekly Iyengar yoga class for 12 weeks, the other half read an information booklet on fall prevention. At the end of the 12 weeks, the researchers compared the two groups on their ability to complete some functional tests of balance and mobility.

The researchers found the group that took part in yoga practice could perform significantly faster in tests involving standing and sitting down quickly without using their arms for support. The yoga group also walked faster in a walking test and stood on one leg for longer, indicating improved balance. Safe and fun for the older participants, attendance was good.

In a study looking at balance and mobility in people 68 and older, published in *The Journals of Gerontology* in 2013, 54 community seniors participated in a 12-week, twice-weekly Iyengar yoga program focused on standing postures. The balance of the intervention group significantly improved compared with control group.

Yep, yoga keeps you young. Writes Sting, an avid Ashtanga yogi: "If anything, it's reversing my aging process. I can now do things with my body that I wouldn't even have thought possible when I was an athletic teenager."

Let's now explore our third power sense, the tactile and its role in yoga practice.

RECAP

PROPRIOCEPTION. Located in our joints, muscles, tendons and ligaments, proprioceptive receptors give us our sense of body position and body awareness. This information enables us to move, plan and make adjustments (coordinate movements) without using vision.

GRAND MODULATOR. Proprioception gets us quickly into that "just right place," calming us when hyper and revving us up when lethargic.

Chemical Balance. Proprioceptive input releases serotonin and dopamine. Serotonin and dopamine wash away cortisol and adrenaline, involved in the fight/flight response of the sympathetic nervous system.

Flying High. When released in large amounts, as happens during intense yoga practice serotonin produces a rush that translates into an emotional high.

Endorphins. Along with releasing serotonin, yoga practice stimulates the pituitary (third eye) gland to release endorphins.

HOW YOGA CREATES SPACE. In yoga practice, proprioceptive input comes from the repetitive flow of postures, to the changing body positions while flowing through the poses, to the compression of muscles and joints in bends, twists, turns and balancing poses.

- Pulling (flexion). Isometric postures pull, like Upward-Facing-Dog, Bow pose, Dancer pose, Pigeon, and seated forward folds.

- Pushing (extension). Weight bearing one legged or arm balancing poses and inversions push.

A Milder Buzz. Relatively easy poses, like the Triangle involve much pushing and pulling into the joints and muscles for heavy work.

LOCATION OF PROPRIOCEPTORS. Proprioceptors are located throughout the body. Major clusters reside at the soles of our feet, ankles, hips, spine (to help with spinal stability), and neck. Particularly important are the proprioceptors in the neck and ankles, both significant for yoga practice.

SENSE OF PLACE IN SPACE

Good Proprioception. Some people have great proprioception and move purposefully, gracefully, and rhythmically. They feel well connected to their bodies.

Poor Proprioception. Those with poor proprioception lack good body awareness and don't experience living in three dimensions.

Hypotonia. Hypotonia, or low tone makes it hard to fight gravity and you tend to slouch, lean and shuffle. You must put in much more effort than others to build muscle. Moving through asanas increases muscle tone and "wakes up" the muscles to decrease hypotonia.

AGE & PROPRIOCEPTION. As we grow older, proprioception deteriorates and causes joints to deteriorate. Balance too becomes harder. Regular yoga practice improves balance to keep you young.

CHAPTER 6

TACTILE SENSE: FEELING THE VIBES

"There is more power in a good strong hug than a thousand meaningful words."

~ANN HOOD

I flop forward in child's pose, resting after doing a strenuous handstand against the wall.

I feel a body behind me. Then, the soothing sensation of deep pressure as James, a tall, muscular guy, drapes his body backward over mine to get my forehead closer to my knees.

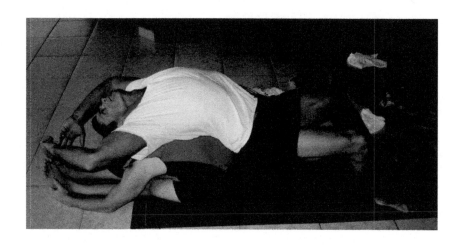

Ahhh. A bear hug.

"Don't get up!" my brain screams.

Little in life gets us into that just right place quicker than a bear hug. Deep pressure into the proprioceptors defines our edges, connecting us to self, to the earth, to others. "Safe," purrs the brain.

The more pressure—the bear hug versus the handshake—the more intense the somatosensory (tactile and proprioceptive) input and the more powerful the effect. "*Hold* me!" we beg when held lightly.

The tactile sense is our third power sense. Tactile sensation happens via touch receptors in multiple skin layers that convey information about: pressure (light, deep); pain; temperature (hot, cold); and vibration. Sending a wealth of information to our brains, we use almost all of these cells when we take a yoga class: the pressure of our hands pushing down in Downward-Facing Dog; the squishiness of our mat under our feet; the wetness of sweat dripping down our bodies; the touch of our teacher as he coaches us through a posture; the humid warmth in the room; the breeze from the open window.

These receptors allow us to discriminate touching, a far sense, and being touched, a primal near sense.

DEEP PRESSURE TOUCH

Tactile receptors for pressure, or deep touch, known as discriminative touch allow us to recognize the "feel" of things, without looking or thinking about what our fingers, hands, or feet are pressing against. "I'm safe!" deep pressure touch whispers, calming us to serene contentment.

Yoga & Deep Pressure

How much deep pressure can you get in a non-contact activity like yoga, you might wonder? A good part of the class consists of standing poses that involve mostly pressure into hands and feet. True. But hands and feet provide more sensation than you might realize.

As represented in the sensory homunculus, palms and feet have a greater number of neurons and dendrites. A distorted representation of the human body, the sensory homunculus is based on a neurological "map" of the areas and proportions of the human brain dedicated to processing motor functions, or sensory functions, for different parts of the body.

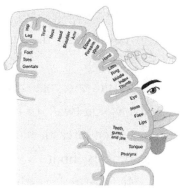

Wikimedia

Weight bearing into hands and feet in poses like Downward-Facing Dog can exert strong touch pressure, calming and grounding you. Perhaps this relaxing effect on the nervous system is why Downward-Facing Dog has become the very symbol of yoga.

Many poses cover greater body surface than hands and feet. In seated poses you get pressure to butt and back of legs. In prone poses like Boat, you get pressure *into the abdomen*. In poses like Dolphin, you get pressure *into the forehead*.

In supine poses like Savasana, you lie flat on your back for typically 5-10 minutes with the whole back body pushed into the floor, creating intense relaxation.

"...when I'm trapped in the most overwhelming sensory moments," writes Rachel Schneider in *Making Sense*, "nothing feels quite as right as hitting the deck, or sprawling out on the floor.... on my back with my legs and arms splayed out like Da Vinci's famed Vitruvian Man. By hitting the deck someone with proprioceptive issues can press skin and joints against the solid ground connecting the entire physical self to the still, strong earth." (p. 114).

In Anuttara yoga, many poses are practiced lying on back or belly, as you twist, or bend leg or arm. These full body poses provide deep pressure to a large skin surface, adding much somatosensory input.

My favorite is resting on the belly, arms at the side at a 45 degree angle, head turned to one side in "Sleeping Serpent," the hard floor providing deep pressure touch to the whole front of the body. I feel the pressure especially against cheek, breastbone, pelvic bones and knees, almost as if I'm resting against another body, sans the heat. As I inhale, I feel my front body expand into the floor, and my back and side ribs expanding to the sides. We lie in the pose for several minutes and, eyes closed, I go into a trance.

This pose is done throughout the hour and half class to reset and go deeper within, one of the perks of the practice for me. Past childhood, how often do we get to lie on the floor on our bellies?

Props

You get further deep pressure from the use of yoga props, like bolsters, blocks and sandbags, and from working against the wall, especially in Iyengar. You get deep pressure, as well, from yoga adjustments and from partner yoga. I'll talk extensively about this in chapter eleven.

Teacher Adjustments

I'm lying in Savasana at the end of a Power Vinyasa yoga class. James pushes down my shoulders with his powerful hands, throwing me into deeper meditation. His touch probably initiated Theta brain waves.

When done with firm pressure and not defended against, adjustments add touch pressure.

In a small class, the teacher might want to try and touch everyone who wishes it as soon as possible. This is to release oxytocin for connectedness, serotonin as a mood regulator, and dopamine to neutralize emotions, all three released in just the right combination to create a serene, safe haven.

Chemical Buzz

All this deep pressure during yoga class, along with proprioceptive feedback from muscles and joints boosts serotonin production (described in chapter nine in talking about yoga and depression), as well as dopamine and oxytocin. As we know: serotonin uplifts our mood; dopamine makes us feel rewarded; and oxytocin, the "cuddle" hormone makes us feel bonded and less fearful.

Practice yoga in your backyard or along the ocean and you'll further increase serotonin. UV light from the sun when absorbed through your skin produces Vitamin D. Vitamin D promotes serotonin production. This is why being outside in nature uplifts mood.

To get a hint at the power of serotonin and touch, do this if you have a pet. Hold your hand over Maxie or Molly and notice your state of being. Now touch your pet. Did you feel an immediate calming? This is from serotonin release. Interestingly, researchers have found no increase when petting a strange dog.

LIGHT TOUCH

"Get over your self-consciousness about others touching you," said a clueless teacher to a yoga student. In response to another students' long hair having graced her arm, she had rubbed the spot and moved her mat to the corner.

Light touch, not self-consciousness spurred her defensive response.

Receptors that register light touch evoke a primitive, alarm system to alert you of danger: a bug might be crawling up your leg; a stranger in the crowd might be picking your pocket.

As a warning, these receptors release arousing brain chemicals like cortisol, sparking fear. The sympathetic nervous system goes into action and stress chemicals like cortisol course through the bloodstream to alert you to pay attention.

Until you know what's touching you, you can't focus on anything else. In the very least, you become jumpy. Some touchy people become aggressive and have been known to instinctively punch a stranger in a crowd whose hand graces their shoulder.

In yoga, light touch happens if a teacher adjusts you with feather-like fingers. I cringe when this happens. After class I will politely inform the teacher of the need for firm touch and why.

Light touch might happen as well if mats are too close and bodies swipe each other. This is not uncommon in a crowded class. In a posture like the Supine Spinal Twist, someone's hand invariably lightly touches your arm, side or leg.

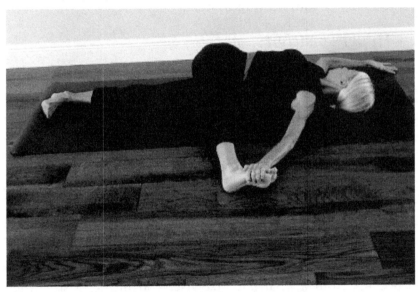
(Jen)

This quote from Temple Grandin, the autistic savant who became a professor of animal science and whose story was immortalized on HBO in the film, *Temple Grandin,* sums up the difference between deep pressure touch and light touch.

"Deep touch pressure is the type of surface pressure that is exerted in most types of firm touching, holding, stroking, petting of animals, or swaddling. In contrast, light touch pressure is a more superficial stimulation of the skin, such as tickling, very light touch, or moving hairs on the skin. In animals, the tickle of a fly landing on the skin may cause a cow to kick, but the firm touch of the farmer's hands quiets her" (cited in *Sensory-Enhanced Yoga*, p. 153).

Different Strokes for Different Folks

Does light touch annoy you? Do certain textures give you the heebie jeebies? The answer will vary according to the arousability of your nervous system.

Hypersensitivity

My yoga teacher Judy was born touchy. Her grandmother nicknamed her "Touch-me-not." How did she become a yoga teacher and spend much time touching others? She got over her touchiness through a great "sensory diet." Ballet lessons began at four. At age 30, she added yoga and has practiced daily since.

If you are hyper-sensitive to tactile sensation, ordinary touch feels aversive and instigates a range of responses from annoyance to panic, depending on level of sensitivity.

You might cringe when cuddled, kissed and lightly touched, especially from a stranger. Likewise, you might bristle when wearing clothes of rough texture, tight clothes, bras, nylons, waist/wrist bands, socks with seams, or jewelry.

Hair touching your face, cutting hair or nails, taking baths and showers, waves whacking you at the beach, walking on sand, grass, stones, concrete—all might send shocks surging through your system. In yoga, you forego the fashion of tights and spandex bra-like tops for loose, soft cotton or hemp clothing. Feeling too much pain, and miserable in heat or cold, you look for yoga class neither air-conditioned nor heated.

During class, you need a large bubble of space between your body and another's. If approached too closely, you might panic.

One day, arriving late to a crowded class, I asked a new guy to move his mat so I could squeeze in. That would have placed me within around two feet of his mat. Glaring at me, he moved his mat— out the door!

My guess is that he was tactile defensive and such proximity was too close for comfort.

DIGGING DEEPER

Boundaries of self may extend well beyond the body into an invisible bubble of space—our territory. In yoga class, our space is defined by our mat. It separates our space from others. Etiquette dictates that people are not to put their feet on our mat.

People cannot stretch their limbs into "our" yoga space. If needing to leave during class, most will carefully tip-toe through rows of mats, weaving around water bottles and towels to avoid stepping on our mat or invading our space.

BEING MINDFUL

Experienced yoga teachers who adjust during class will often ask permission first of a new student if it's okay to do so. It's not just that one might be "touchy," injuries may counter-indicate adjustments.

At the front desk at Yoga South are coasters to place next to your mat that say, "Don't adjust me."

Following head trauma, I became the artful dodger of light touch, or roughness against my skin.

While finishing *Too Loud, too Bright,* I was exceptionally wired, my whole body pulsing and pounding, pulling and surging. I would drag myself away from my computer and to yoga class, hoping for relief. While lying in Child's Pose, in which I spent half of that class, I saw my teacher's feet paddling toward me. My hand shot up. *"Don't touch me,"* I muttered. His face fell in confusion and hurt.

Too over the edge for even yoga to help, I left class and retreated to my bed—lights off, no sound, not even music, and curled into the fetal tuck. After a few hours, I slipped from extreme overload to tolerable head pressure, tolerable eyestrain, tolerable light-headedness, and slipped into a soothing, warm, lavender infused bath.

Today my defensiveness is mild and manageable: a crowded class with people infringing my space bothers me little, while adjustments are welcomed and desired as long as touch is firm.

My usual attire consists of a tight, yoga cotton or bamboo top. During class, I'm unaware of the tightness though I throw the top off the minute I get home. My favored bottoms are semi-tight bamboo Capri pants that I can wear all day. Tags in my clothing still bother me and are removed, though many people do so.

How much might yoga have contributed to a decrease in defensiveness? I suspect a great deal. Except during times of severe overload, yoga quelled my jumpiness, even if only for the hour and half of class, and a bit of time after ... before the world again attacked me.

During the practice itself, the stillness within postures offered respite from sensory input. In fact, as I mentioned earlier shutting out sensory stimulation is one of the eight limbs of yoga from the Yoga Sutras.

Some poses especially foster sensory withdrawal, like Child, Savasana, and the restorative "Sleeping Serpent," my favorite with so much of my body surface pressing against the floor. Unless your nervous system is damaged, as happens with autism, tactile receptors stop sending signals to the central nervous system after a few seconds of stillness, according to David Coulter, author of *Anatomy of Hatha Yoga*.

Hyposensitivity

Some people register on the other end of the spectrum and are hypo-responsive to sensation. They might barely register sensation and miss out on tactile information.

For instance, your feet might not realize the yoga floor is dirty, or a bug is crawling up your arm. To better tune into the world, you bolster sensation into the skin by wearing tight clothes with rough, fuzzy, or uneven texture. Some wear extra jewelry.

Craving another's body against yours, you tend to get up close and personal, even with non-intimates. In yoga, you might invade the other's space, placing your mat inappropriately close to another's or your towel or water bottle in the other's space. The latter drives me crazy in large part, as mentioned, because it's a visual distraction.

Rarely do you complain of being cold and don't easily detect pain. In yoga, you will push past pain. In fact, you may enjoy pain for its intensity and adorn your body with tattoos and pierce your nose with a gold ring.

Still, this is not a sensory processing problem unless it interferes in everyday life. For my hypo-sensitive mother, it did. As mentioned, she made little sense of her world. She would hang up damp clothes in her closet, squished among dry clothes, not having detected the wetness. After she washed the dishes, dirt remained because her hands didn't detect the residue as I mentioned earlier.

Low Serotonin

One reason for poor sensory awareness is low serotonin. To raise serotonin and calm, some become self-abusive as self-abuse raises serotonin. In the extreme some people bang their heads; pull out their hair; cut their skin; and seek and enjoy rough or abusive sex.

Now that the role of the power senses in yoga bliss is elucidated, let's look at the other important component: pranayama breathing.

RECAP

DEEP PRESSURE TOUCH. Tactile receptors for pressure, or deep touch, known as discriminative touch allow us to recognize the "feel" of things, without looking or thinking about what our fingers, hands, or feet are pressing against, calming us.

YOGA & DEEP PRESSURE

Poses. You get deep pressure during standing poses from pressure into hands and feet. In seated poses you get pressure to butt and back of legs. In prone poses like Boat, you get pressure into the abdomen. In poses like Dolphin, you get pressure into the forehead.

Props. You get further deep pressure from the use of yoga props, like bolsters, blocks and sandbags, and from working against the wall, especially in Iyengar.

Teacher Adjustments. When done with firm pressure and not defended against, adjustments add touch pressure.

Chemical Buzz. Sensations of deep pressure and proprioceptive feedback from our muscles and joints release a Chemical Buzz of hormones: serotonin uplifts our mood; dopamine makes us feel rewarded; oxytocin, the "cuddle" hormone makes us feel bonded and less fearful.

LIGHT TOUCH. Receptors that register light touch evoke a primitive, alarm system to alert you of danger: a bug might be crawling up your leg; a stranger in the crowd might be picking your pocket. In yoga, light touch happens if a teacher adjusts you with feather-like fingers or mats are too close and bodies swipe each other.

DIFFERENT STROKES FOR DIFFERENT FOLKS

Hypersensitivity. Ordinary touch feels aversive and instigates a range of responses from annoyance to panic, depending on level of sensitivity. If approached too closely during yoga class, you might panic.

Hyposensitivity. Those who are hypo-responsive to sensation barely register sensation. In yoga, they may miss out on tactile information like whether the floor is dirty.

CHAPTER 7

THE CONSCIOUS BREATH

"Breath is the king of mind."

~B.K.S. IYENGAR

I'm leaning to the right in Triangle. Behind me I hear a familiar "Woosh. Woosh." It's James breathing in and out like Star War's Darth Vader. He rotates my left shoulder and pulls my left arm further over my head to get me into a correct stance. The sound of "Whoosh, Whoosh" hums in my ear.

From Ashtanga tradition, "Ujjayi" Pranayama (VictoriousBreath) is deep-chest breathing made by slightly constricting the back of the throat as you breathe in and out through the nose, making breath softly audible. Ujjayi breath is used throughout Ashtanga and Vinyasa, the rhythm of inhalation and exhalation connecting you to the flow of the postures until the final resting pose in Savasana—the "dessert" Pose.

"I don't hear you breathing" James will say throughout the practice to remind us to return to the slight woosh sound of breathing in this manner.

Ashtanga teachers espouse that the deep and rhythmic breath fuels the inner energetic flames, heating and healing the body.

At the same time, hearing your breathing, with its rhythmical and predictable nature calms and focuses you on the present moment. Being present, or mindful, encourages "flow." Flow is a state of total absorption where we are so engrossed in a task we lose track of everything else around us, and where, according to numerous scientific studies we're happiest.

I'm in awe of those in class whose Darth Vader breath I can hear. I try but, even after years of practicing, the sound of my breath is barely audible.

I was never a good breather. My father was a champion swimmer but couldn't teach me the basic swimming crawl because every time I put my head in the water I had to gasp for air. As an anxious adolescent, I would gasp for breath in social situations.

This lung restriction likely came from lordosis of my spine (an exaggerated lumbar curve), along with an exaggerated curve in my neck (lordosis of the cervical neck), both a result of forceps at birth.

An exaggerated lumbar curve tilts the pelvis forward and decreases range of motion for the lower lumbar spine, shortening the latissimus and lower back muscles. This shortens the diaphragm and limits its range of motion. At the same time, the exaggerated curve in my neck compressed my larynx, further restricting breathing. To compound the problem, I breathe primarily through my left lung since my accident, and my right lung always feels somewhat congested and burning.

After starting neurocranial restructuring, I noticed that I was breathing more deeply during yoga practice and felt more relaxed.

Hmmm. What had NCR done?

A few months into the treatment I had my answer. I was looking in the mirror. I thought I had lost weight as my figure looked firmer and more defined and I looked better in my clothes. I turned to my side and my mouth fell open. My sway back was far straighter! Still somewhat arched, but a far less overtly obvious curve. In fact, other than my yoga teachers who, in adjusting me will tell me to pull in my abdomen to straighten out my back, most who look at me feel I have great posture.

With a straighter posture, I had less breathing restriction and pranayama was now doing its wonders on my nervous system.

CONSCIOUS BREATHING

Ujjayi breathing is one form of *Pranayama,* or conscious control of the breath.

At once uplifting and calming, Pranayama is at the heart of and unique to yoga practice. It forges the mind-body connection by bridging the active asanas and the internal or mental practice. "Practice is about breathing," says Judy. "If you're not consciously breathing, you're not doing yoga."

3-Part Breath

Pranayama consists of a 3-part breath. You breathe slowly and deeply first by expanding the abdomen, the middle rib cage, and then the upper chest. Then you breathe out in reverse, from top to bottom, pulling in the abdomen at the end to empty the lungs completely.

Studies show that in this 3-part breath you take in and give out seven times as much air—that means seven times the oxygen than in a shallow breath. Over time, this breathing pattern continues for many off the mat and becomes your routine way of breathing.

CALMING THE NERVOUS SYSTEM

State of mind depends on quality of breath. At the first sign of stress or anxiety, the arousing sympathetic nervous system (SNS) kicks in and breathing changes. You gasp, suck in your abdomen, and breathe high into your chest with short, shallow spurts to ready your body for quick flight.

When the stressor passes, the parasympathetic nervous system (PNS) kicks in to slow breathing and signal our body to relax. It's spurred into action especially by deep breathing, as a neurotransmitter called bradykinin releases when you inhale deeply all the way to the top of the lungs.

Slow breathing shifts activity in the brain from the medulla oblongata, the lowest part of the brainstem to the cerebral cortex where you have conscious control of breathing. At the same time, the shift to the PNS reduces cortisol, lowers blood pressure, elevates oxytocin and endorphins, and lowers the heart rate.

Biological evolution designed us this way: a quick spurt of activity and, when the danger passes, homeostasis. But in our wired, fast-paced society, a new stressor might jump at you before you've recovered from the previous one, like leaving a hectic day of work to drive home in traffic while listening to fire alarms on CNN. As a result, many of us remain in the flight/fight mode and rapid breathing becomes our "normal."

During yoga, if you continue to breathe on autopilot rather than consciously, tension remains in your body and you create holding patterns that keep your muscles constricted and tense. This was me for years after my accident. Changing breathing patterns was difficult because of my previously mentioned problem with lordosis, and because the resulting shift of my body over to the right interfered further with breathing; taking in a full breath took concentration.

With NCR therapy realigning my skull and helping to straighten out my body, allowing me to consciously initiate pranayama breathing more easily, I broke through my pattern of constant tension. Now, in class, I calm after a few minutes of pranayama and will do Ujjai breathing spontaneously during a good part of Vinyasa.

Unless you're very stressed or anxious, or have structural or physiological breathing restrictions, studies have found that consciously taking in several full deep breathes shifts your body into the parasympathetic mode *in as little as 90 seconds*. This happens unconsciously.

Why 90 seconds? Perhaps it's because when we focus on taking in a deep breath, we interrupt our monkey mind, where thoughts swing from one branch to the other, allowing us to shift into the parasympathetic mode.

"Pay attention to breath and feel mind chatter settle," says Frankie as I sit in Easy Pose at the back of the mat, hands resting on thighs at the start of the class."

THE SUN
SALUTATION

1. exhale

2. inhale

3. exhale

4. inhale

5. retain

6. exhale

7. inhale

8. exhale

9. inhale

10. exhale

11. inhale

12. exhale,
inhale and begin
again at 1.

DIGGING DEEPER

Emotions stay in our head and bodies for 90 seconds. If you are steaming because your spouse didn't notice your new hairdo, that fury will last longer only if you feed it with ruminations: "He's so self-involved." "He only cares about himself....." you mutter. But if the phone rings after 90 seconds, and it's your sister telling you that she's pregnant after years of trying, the ruminations stop and your brain will rid itself of the heated anger.

This "90 Second Rule" is the insight of Dr. Jill Bolte Taylor, author of Stroke of Insight. Here's how she explains it: "When a person has a reaction to something in their environment, there's a 90 second chemical process that happens in the body; after that, any remaining emotional response is just the person choosing to stay in that emotional loop."

"The only doorway into the nervous system without involving the higher brain is breath and movement," says Judy. This makes conscious breathing in yoga practice a powerful means for shifting state of being.

Science concurs. In a 2011 analysis of yoga therapy in the treatment of psychiatric disorders, published in *Primary Care Companion CNS Disorders* the researchers found yoga breathing an outstanding therapy in treating anxiety and post-traumatic stress disorder. Stated the authors, "Yoga may provide an inexpensive, effective alternative to common treatments presently used in the treatment of psychiatric disorders."

A study at the University of California in San Diego, conducted by psychologist David Shannahoff-Khalsa, found yoga breathing techniques to significantly decrease the symptoms of obsessive-compulsive disorder. Of eight adults who completed a one-year course of yogic breathing techniques, five were able to discontinue their medication (fluoxetine) and two others drastically reduced the dosage.

Another study showed that slow, deep breathing alone resulted in a significant reduction in menopausal hot flashes.

Yoga teacher Richard Rosen seems to have breathing and mental state down to a science. In a 2007 article online in *Yoga Journal,* Rosen suggests that to calm anxiety, you purposely lengthen exhalations; to alleviate dullness and fatigue, you lengthen inhalations; to lift a blue mood you equalize the lengths of your inhalations and exhalations.

Still, none of these findings should imply that pranayama is a panacea for curing stress, anxiety and depression. These conditions have multiple causes, and need to be attacked on many fronts. In addition to yoga asanas and pranayama, it's important to have a positive mindset, eat whole foods that feed the brain, and reduce stress. Depending on the level of dysfunction, therapy and/or meds may be necessary.

DIFFERENT STYLES, DIFFERENT PRANAYAMA

Different styles of yoga incorporate pranayama differently. In Ashtanga and Vinyasa, you use Ujjayi breath throughout as you flow through the postures. Inhalations correspond with upward movements, exhalations with downward movements. Note for instance, the breathing pattern in a Sun Salutation.

THE SUN SALUTATION

1. exhale
2. inhale
3. exhale
4. inhale
5. retain
6. exhale
7. inhale
8. exhale
9. inhale
10. exhale
11. inhale
12. exhale, inhale and begin again at 1.

During Vinyasa, James will punctuate the intensity of the poses with breathing breaks in Mountain or Child Pose, where he tells us to "breathe and reset."

In Bikram yoga, classes begin with *Bellows Breath*. Standing in Mountain Pose, you inhale through the nose with the *woosh* of Ujjayi breathing for a count of six. Fingers are interlaced and elbows lifted out to the sides until they stretch up to the sides of your head. You open your mouth and slowly drop your head back exhaling to the account of six, letting the sound of 'haaaaaa' increase the force of this breath. This breathing exercise transfers oxygen to your muscles and organs, expands your lungs, and puts your mind at ease to increase focus throughout the practice.

In Kundalini yoga, you coordinate breathing with movement. For instance, you will inhale as you turn your body to the right and exhale as you turn your body to the left. Typically you begin slow and quicken your movement and breathing to a speedy pace, energizing you. Breathing practices like Breath of Fire, a rapid diaphragmatic breath are integrated as well into the classes to charge your system even more. In fact, in Kundalini practice breathing is emphasized more so than precision of movement or technique.

In Anuttara Raja class, pranayama is used extensively. As mentioned, class begins in Easy Pose where you focus on breathing the 3-part yoga breath. After moving into Child, followed by a twist to each side in this pose, you move to "Toe Cruncher," where you practice typically the Bellows Breath, the same pranayama that begins Bikram.

After a few more poses, you move into Cat/Cow. In Cat you inhale deeply and in Cow breathe out forcefully and fully—hah!

(Jen)

At intervals throughout Anuttara Raja practice, you rest in Easy Pose to focus exclusively on breathing and, at the end of class, take in and expel three full slow deep breaths before collapsing gratefully into Savasana.

The breathing practices, the dark, hot room, the soft meditative music of Craig Pruess creates a warm, deep, quiet, still practice that makes Anuttara Raja yoga an hour and a half meditation.

Alternate Nostril Breathing (ANB)

Not all breathing practices take me quickly to that just right place. Bellows Breath at the beginning of Anuttara Raja does little to quiet my quivering insides, probably because it is stimulating rather than calming. What does immediately calm me is ANB, which often follows the Bellows Breath or is weaved in later in the practice.

ANB involves breathing through one nostril at a time and alternating sides.

Research has found right nostril dominance stimulates the arousal-producing sympathetic nervous system, as does inhaling (when anxious, we gasp for air); and left nostril dominance elicits the relaxation-producing parasympathetic system, as does exhaling. "Breathe out and let go of muscular tension, worries, fears, wants," says Philip during Anuttara Raja.

Doing alternative nostril breathing balances the two sides of the brain. Of particular interest is a research study that suggests ANB enhances body awareness. Reported in 1997 in *Psychological Reports*, the study found that using alternate nostril breathing to deepen and slow breathing rate increased spatial memory in 10-to 17-year olds. Increased spatial awareness relates to field independence, the ability to accurately orient and maneuver in space, in other words to be centered and grounded in space. This makes practicing ANB an important opportunity to enhance body awareness.

VAGUS NERVE

The vagus nerve. If you haven't yet heard of it, pay close attention. It's the secret to psychological nirvana.

To achieve stability and balance, to remain calm, cool and collected, to keep a level head we want to tap into our parasympathetic nervous system (PNS).

The route to the PNS? The vagus nerve.

The longest cranial nerve, the vagus nerve runs from the brain to the heart to the gastrointestinal tract to brain, making it a key pathway of interoception (internal body awareness). Interfacing with parasympathetic control of the heart, lungs, and digestive tract, its main job is the relaxation response, telling your heart to slow down, your breathing to slow and deepen, and your gut to rest and digest. If you think of stress as driving with the foot slammed down on the gas pedal, the vagus nerve is the brake.

HRV: Heart Rate Variability

Vagal tone is measured in the changes in heart rate that occur with the breath. This irregularity between heartbeats is known as heart rate variability (HRV) or respiratory sinus arrhythmia. Healthy vagal tone involves a slight increase in heart rate on the inhalation and a decrease of heart rate when you exhale, optimally balancing parasympathetic and sympathetic nervous system activity.

Those who have higher HRV move more easily from excitement to relaxed and recover more easily from stress. In other words, a higher HRV equals modulation and emotional self-regulation.

When breathing becomes shallow, the vagus nerve is inflamed and the body is in fight or flight mode. If stress becomes chronic, as it did with me you may experience a stiff neck, throat, and jaw muscles that, in turn, can make it harder to take in a deep breath. Not only was my neck stiff and my throat constricted but my jaw muscles were extremely tight.

The stiffness and tightness occurs because the vagus nerve influences the hyoid bone, which supports the larynx and trachea, the jaw pulling open and the protrusion of the tongue. Stress and resulting stiffness in your shoulders and neck can throw off muscle coordination of the hyoid, as when food seems to go down the wrong pipe and you get into a coughing fit.

Healthy vagal tone reflects a balance between the sympathetic and parasympathic nervous systems. Too much SNS and too little PNS and we feel restless, agitated, stressed, and, in those vulnerable, could lead to panic attack. Too much PNS and too little SNS and we feel slow, lethargic, apathetic, and in the extreme numb. A balanced vagal tone makes for feeling "just right."

Yoga Boosts Vagal Tone

Research has found that slow, rhythmic, pranayama breathing increases healthy vagal tone. At the same time, yoga postures that open across your chest and throat, like Cobra, Bow, Camel, Cow and Fish gently stimulate the vagus nerve. These poses in turn open up the rib cage to encourage better breathing, while moving through Cat/Cow helps to connect you with the vagus nerve as it passes through your belly.

A 2015 study out of Taiwan examined the effects of a 12-week yoga intervention on work-related stress, stress adaptation, and balance of autonomic nerve activities in mental health workers, as measured by HRV. The results showed that the mental health professionals in the yoga group experienced a significant reduction in work-related stress and better adaptation to stress.

Other Ways to Enhance Vagal Tone

You can also increase vagal tone by humming, and by chanting *om*, as some yoga practices do. My Iyengar classes open with three *oms*, while Anuttara Raja ends with one *om*.

You can also just smile. "Soften your jaw muscles," James repeats throughout the class and I do. Unknowingly, this simple action brightens my mood. Since the vagus nerve extends into the muscles of the face, relaxing the muscles of your face and slightly turning up your lips increases vagal tone, changing your mental state and engaging what Dr. Stephen Porges calls the "social nervous system," the most evolved branch of the vagus nerve.

Pranayama & Oxytocin

Pranayama breathing calms also because stimulating the vagus nerve dampens activity in the amygdala and releases oxytocin.

Deep breathing also warms the body, and warmth is one of the key elements that allows for release of oxytocin.

SENSORY INPUT

Do vestibular and proprioceptive inputs play a role in the quality of our breath?

Indeed.

When your teacher says, "Focus on your breath," the focus is on your respiratory muscles activating and relaxing, in other words proprioceptive input.

What about vestibular input? What's its role? The vestibular system regulates autonomic arousal by stimulating the vagal system to inhibit the sympathetic system to achieve a much calmer state. As breathing is tied to vagal input, so is the vestibular sense.

Now that we have an idea of the power of pranayama to relax the nervous system, let's peak into the brain to better understand our senses.

RECAP

CONSCIOUS BREATHING

Pranayama, or conscious control of the breath is at the heart of and unique to yoga practice. It forges the mind-body connection by bridging the active asanas and the internal or mental practice.

"Ujjayi" Pranayamareath. Deep-chest breathing made by slightly constricting the back of the throat as you breathe in and out through the nose, making breath softly audible.

3-Part Breath. You breathe slowly and deeply first by expanding the abdomen, the middle rib cage, and then the upper chest. Then you breathe out in reverse, from top to bottom, pulling in the abdomen at the end to empty the lungs completely.

CALMING THE NERVOUS SYSTEM. At the first sign of stress or anxiety, the arousing sympathetic nervous system (SNS) kicks in and breathing changes. You gasp, suck in your abdomen, and breathe high into your chest with short, shallow spurts to ready your body for quick flight. When the stressor passes, the parasympathetic nervous system (PNS) kicks in to slow breathing and signal our body to relax. During yoga, you breathe consciously to tap into the PSN.

DIFFERENT STYLES, DIFFERENT PRANAYAMA

Ashtanga and Vinyasa. You use Ujjayi breath throughout as you flow through the postures. Inhalations correspond with upward movements, exhalations with downward movements.

Bikram Yoga. Classes begin with *Bellows Breath*.

Kundalini Yoga. You coordinate breathing with movement. For instance, you will inhale as you turn your body to the right and exhale as you turn your body to the left.

Alternate Nostril Breathing. More meditative classes like Anutarra Raja often employ ANB. ANB involves breathing through one nostril at a time and alternating sides. Doing alternative nostril breathing balances the two sides of the brain.

VAGUS NERVE

Interfacing with parasympathetic control of the heart, lungs, and digestive tract, the main job of the vague nerve is the relaxation response, telling your heart to slow down, your breathing to slow and deepen, and your gut to rest and digest.

Heart Rate Variability (HRV). Vagal tone is measured in the changes in heart rate that occur with the breath. This irregularity between heartbeats is known as heart rate variability (HRV) or respiratory sinus arrhythmia.

Healthy Vagal Tone. Involves a slight increase in heart rate on the inhalation and a decrease of heart rate when you exhale, optimally balancing parasympathetic and sympathetic nervous system activity.

Boosting Vagal Tone:

- Pranayama Breathing

- Humming and chanting

- Smiling

PRANAYAMA & OXYTOCIN. Pranayama breathing calms also because stimulating the vagus nerve dampens activity in the amygdala and releases oxytocin.

PART II

THE SCIENCE

"It is through the alignment of the body that I discovered the alignment of my mind, self, and intelligence."

~B.K.S. IYENGAR

CHAPTER 8

YOGA ON THE BRAIN

"Yoga is like music. The rhythm of the body, the melody of the mind, and the harmony of the soul create the symphony of life."

~B.K.S. IYENGAR

In 1999, after a week of intensive treatment in sensory integration therapy at the Ayres Clinic in Torrance, California, Patti Oetter sent me home with a sensory diet... and a caveat.

"The sensory diet is only half the equation," she said. "The other half is cognition. I can tell you what to do. Whether or not you do it, is up to you."

In other words, she gave me the "body." But without adding my "mind" to the equation, all would be for naught as I wouldn't follow through.

Luckily, I was born with "grit," the persistence gene (an actual gene!), which means I doggedly pursue my goal until I've achieved it or have exhausted all resources.

Even were I not born with this gene, my yoga practice would push me past a limiting mindset. First through mindfulness and then because yoga rewires the brain to a more positive framework.

Let's explore.

MINDFULNESS

Unlike other forms of low impact physical activity, yoga teachers encourage mindfulness. "Stay present" James will say throughout class to remind us to focus on what's going on in our bodies, not on the veggies and avocado dip we will chomp on when we finish practice. In fact, without the sustained intention of focusing on the present, and calming the mind, you're not practicing yoga but just going through the motions.

Being mindful taps into the neocortex or thinking brain. The frontal lobes in the cortex are the home of consciousness, the place where thinking allows us to interpret what the senses perceive. Here is where self-talk says, "Okay, calm down. Everything's fine." In other words, the cortex gives us some control or will power over the primal lower messages.

"Yoga has a sly, clever way of short-circuiting the mental patterns that cause anxiety," says Baxter Bell in a quote from "Worry Thwarts," a March 1006 online article in Yoga Journal.

But there's a catch. The cortex works up to speed only when the autonomic nervous system is dialed down to safe mode. In flight-fight, the reptilian, primitive brainstem and limbic emotional brain take over. The cortex becomes too bombarded with sensory information to pay attention because focus and energy get waylaid to sort out what's important and what's not— into real or imagined survival needs. And that trumps thinking.

Cortisol releases and inhibits dopamine, which is required by the higher brain to pay attention and learn.

Here's where yoga power comes in. The enormous input into the vestibular, proprioceptive and tactile systems feed the primitive brain, integrating the senses to work as a team and modulating the autonomic nervous system at the primitive level. No longer needing to focus on putting out fires, the cerebral cortex takes over to influence the lower processes, and mind takes control.

Over time, this control translates to mental control off the mat.

"Yoga," says Philip, "teaches you to walk through life in a conscious manner, smoothing out your path."

A supreme example of the power of sensory input to modulate the nervous system and enhance thinking is James. He has some auditory processing issues and takes a bit of time for him to process spoken information.

But *not* while he's teaching. During class, his mind is clear and focused and rarely does he lose concentration. His memory is sharp as well. Yoga teachers must remember a sequence they give on one side of the body and talk it out on the other side. While teachers routinely forget a pose or two, James seldom does. And he's nearly 60 years old.

What accounts for such clear thinking? During the hour and a half class, he walks around adjusting people using strong muscular input that feeds, modulates, and organizes *his* nervous system. This

allows the thinking CEO neocortex to take command. Though modest by nature, James, with a wry smile admits feeling like a yogi king as he majestically strides the honey colored golden wooden floor, teaching, demonstrating, adjusting.

(James)

TOP-DOWN VS BOTTOM-UP PROCESSING

The body is the gateway to the mind. But the mind is also the gateway to the body. By incorporating a focus on present awareness of bodily sensations in the asanas, positive suggestions, and inspirational words into the practice, yoga addresses the nervous system from both "bottom-up"—*using the power of the body to influence the mind*—and "top-down"—*using the power of the mind to influence the body.*

The extent of each varies by yoga style. Styles that focus primarily on the exercise component of yoga, like Bikram and Vinyasa, emphasize bottom-up processing. "Lift your leg with enthusiasm," James will say.

Still, yoga would not be yoga without also incorporating a top-down approach to address the higher self. And so, even in classes with an emphasis on the physical, teachers will weave in top-down processing.

ILLUMINATING

Both top-down and bottom-up processing are outlined in the Yoga Sutras.

Asana (limb 3) and pranayama (limb 4) use bottom-up processing and are at the heart of all yoga practice, as are the top-down processing of focused concentration (limb 6), meditation at the end in Savasana (limb 7), and withdrawal of the senses and focusing inward (limb 5) during meditation.

Limb 1, limb 2, and limb 8 refer to a more transcendent practice and are emphasized throughout spiritually oriented classes like Anuttara Yoga, at its heart Kriya yoga, a practice that focuses not on exercising the body but on enhancing the soul.

Throughout the class, James will say things like, "Don't give into the desire to pull out of the pose. Go to your edge."

And virtually all yoga teachers end the class with brief inspirational thoughts before closing with "Namaste."

My Iyengar class opens with something inspirational. Sometimes it's something from the Yoga Sutras as we sit in Easy Pose or, in Stephanie's class yesterday, something about telomeres (a compound structure at the end of a chromosome), and how creating space in yoga impacts our DNA, extending life.

Yoga changes our DNA? Sounds a bit farfetched. Yet research confirms this. One study published in *Oxidative Medicine and Cellular Longevity* in 2017 found 12-weeks of a yoga and meditation practice increased telomerase activity significantly.

The mean length of telomeres increased also though not significantly.

Whatever that lesson is for the day in Stephanie's class, it will be applied throughout. And so, as we sat in various postures, propped up and around with blocks, blankets, bolsters and straps, Stephanie reminded us how we were lengthening not only our bodies but our telomeres and, in so doing our lives!

More spiritually-oriented yoga classes, like Anuttara Raja infuse more top-down processing, or brain to body. Throughout the hour and a half class, the teacher will spew pearls of wisdom from the *Yoga Sutras* to nurture positive thoughts and attitudes and to stay present and in touch with your feelings.

"You can take one step forward or one step back," says Frankie as we lie in Sleeping Serpent. "It's up to you what you choose." Later in the class he says, "Yoga helps you find your truth, to turn your mind into your best friend rather than your worst enemy."

Looking at the Bright Side

The path we choose to take at any moment can construct a new road by forging a new memory (with positive thinking), or dig us deeper into a pit by repeating old habits (negative thinking). What path we choose gets fortified by the amygdala, which jumps in to attach an emotion to the memory. If our thoughts are naysaying, our body fills with doubt, anxiety or fear.

In yoga, negativity doesn't exist. The practice encourages a more positive outlook on life, fostering much self-growth.

Using the top-down approach, teachers encourage you to focus on the present; negative thinking takes place in the past and future. "Being in the present moment prepares you for the next moment," says Frankie during Anuttara Raja. "But this happens only if you are mindfully present. The past creates depression; the future anxiety."

Teachers will inspire you to do the best *you* can and focus on your own progress; negative thinking happens when you compare yourself to the yoga superstars in the class doing full splits, balancing on their hands, and arching their backs like a Tuscan doorway. Teachers embolden you to feel in control of mind and body; negative thinking happens when you feel others control your life and decision making. And teachers urge grit and persistence; negative thinking leads to procrastination or giving up altogether.

"Don't worry how you look, only how you feel," says Philip. "Think only about being in your own body space," says Frankie. "No more but also no less."

By encouraging you to pay attention to breath, to sensations in your body, you stay present. In the here and now, you are inside your body and out of your head. This keeps introspection, worries and self-assaults to a minimum.

Says Irish actor Colin Farrell about his yoga practice: "It's very easy to live where you remain in your head... and you're concerned about various things and constantly contemplating and so on and so forth, so it takes you out of your head for a while and just puts you back into your body."

Right/Left Brain

Mind chatter comes from too much beta wave activity, as beta waves govern beliefs and attitudes about self in the brain. Mind chatter takes place in the left, logical, thinking-in-words neocortex brain, and fills your head with worries and negativity.

An unchecked neocortex gets us into trouble with excessive mind chatter, as this amusing cartoon demonstrates.

https://hamilton.modoyoga.com/the-neuroscience-behind-Savasana/

By staying present in yoga, your right, creative, intuitive brain takes over, and alpha brain waves dominate stopping negativity.

Nothing illustrates this better than Dr. Jill Bolte Taylor's experience of having a stroke, described in her book *Stroke of Insight*. The stroke involved her left, logical, verbal side. After having woken up in the hospital, she experienced the world through the right hemisphere of her brain. She describes the feeling as "pure Nirvana," feeling "enormous and expansive, like a genie liberated from a bottle... I remember thinking, there's no way I would ever be able to squeeze the enormousness of myself back inside this tiny little body."

Bolte thinks of the right hemisphere as "consciousness, right here, right now," as she explains in an online interview on

HotDoc. "It's bringing information in and processing everything about the current moment. It looks at everything as a collective whole. When we're in that way of being, we feel expansive and open. We're focused on the bigger picture."

Teaching Persistence

Teachers also encourage not giving up.

In Anuttara Raja yoga, you stay in contorted poses for 3-5 minutes. The poses are uncomfortable, some of them excruciatingly so and seconds tick by until the teacher says, "Release." Some people will flop down before the requisite holding time ends. The object is to avoid that.

"The pose begins when you want to get out of it."

~BARON BAPTISTE

To help us sustain the pose, Frankie will tell us to "find comfort in discomfort." These words bolster the fortitude needed to resist the desire to quit the pose. Over time, sustaining the pose and facing the burn rewires your brain to a mindset better able to face life's challenges and difficulties with equanimity (I'll describe rewiring of the brain in detail in a bit).

Soon, you find that you think in a more life affirming *I can do it* mode, enhancing mind/body connection. Over time, confidence, optimism, and hope boost, as many longtime yogis will attest, myself included. Actress Jennifer Aniston credits yoga for making her more confident.

A 2018 study from Germany assessed 93 yoga students' self-centrality and self-enhancement bias before and after practicing yoga. Over a period of 15 weeks, students recruited from eight hatha yoga schools in Germany participated in up to four 90-minute classes focused on postures (asanas), breathing exercises (pranayamas), meditation (dhyana), and relaxation (Savasana). Students perceived yoga to be more central to their identity, reported higher self-esteem and communal narcissism (an inflated sense of one's positive impact on the world).

In her twenties, actress Jessica Biel struggled to find herself. She found it in yoga. "I was searching for my identity as a person, and what defines me," Jessica told WomensHealthMag. com. "And yoga became a space where I can really touch back into myself and my spirituality."

Getting in Touch with Feelings

Classes that encourage a top-down approach foster conscious awareness of feelings and intention to encourage a higher state of consciousness. "Awakening of consciousness," says Frankie, "is awakening of self. Think of practice as an opportunity to reshape and remold your body and mind to break habitual patterns, our addictions. Remember, you can choose your response rather than merely react."

By reinforcing positive behaviors, yoga gives us the tools to break thought and emotional patterns that no longer serve us. This allows the choice of healthier responses when challenges arise, making yoga a powerful practice for health and wellbeing.

Emotional Release

As we bend, twist and stretch muscles, we create space and expand range of motion. As we do, bodily patterns that trap emotional pain shift, unlocking repressed emotions and memories stored all over the body, and painful feelings may release.

Writer Elizabeth Gilbert lost it in her first yoga class from which, as described earlier she almost fled because it was so much *woo woo*. While she was in the twist that launched her to become a yoga fanatic, the teacher "pressed one hand gently on my hip and another on my shoulder to open that twist up just a tiny bit more...and I burst into tears...." she conveyed to Yoga Journal. "As I lay there crying and twisting open, full of longing, full of prayer, full of doubt, full of the wish to be a better human being...full of the sudden and shocking realization that there was a different kind of intelligence in this life, and it could come to us only through the body..."

Powerful emotional reactions erupt especially in Savasana. While focusing on flowing, on breathing, on staying steady enables you to hold it together during the asanas, once you get to stillness, and there is nothing else for the body to do, it all lets loose. Worry and anger, sadness and regret, dread and terror—all spill out as tears mixed with sweat roll down your face.

Years ago, my friend Deborah, a sweet, warm woman burst into tears while lying in Savasana.

I sidled up next to her. "What's wrong?" I asked stroking her shoulder.

Her husband's partners had defrauded him, she told me sobbing and they were broke.

I saw her in class last week and reminded her of that event. She laughed. "Yoga opens everything up. All barriers broke down."

"Yoga helps, more than anything. If you store something heavy emotionally in the mind, it stores as well as the body. So the reverse is true, if you're able to release whatever it is from the body, you can release it from the mind."

~WOODY HARRELSON,
2012 INTERVIEW WITH ORIGIN MAGAZINE

Suddenly bursting into tears can be daunting. To cope with what could be an embarrassing moment, we need a dose of self-compassion. Says Frankie at the beginning of practice, "As you go through the practice today, treat yourself with compassion and kindness. Only by giving ourselves kindness and compassion can we give this to others." In this way, should you become emotional, you'll stroke yourself lovingly on the cheek, rather than lambast yourself for acting like a child during class.

While never bursting into tears during class, I have, during crises lapsed into a twilight nightmare state in Savasana, where I left the mat and entered a hellish dimension with terrifying images. Thrown, I would shake my body and force myself back into reality. "Did I make whimpering or groaning sounds?" I worried. What if I did? Would people laugh at me or show concern? I could use more self-compassion.

How common is losing it in yoga? More common than you might think.

When Philip Christodoulou first began teaching Anuttara Raja, which he created, he was thrown by how people would sob in class and pour out their problems to him. "I was ill prepared to be therapist, priest or Rabbi." And so he began to play the "court jester" during class to lighten things up and discourage emotional outbursts.

Joy also may release. One day while in Savasana at the end of Power Vinyasa yoga, I heard what I thought were little squeaks. Barbara was on the mat next to mine and later confessed she was laughing.

"Why," I asked.

"I felt so happy."

Molecules of Emotion

Some yoga teachers attribute, falsely, emotional outpouring as a release from stored trauma located in the hips.

While it's true we hold tremendous tension in our hips, no scientific evidence exists that we hold emotions there. Emotions may arise at the release of stored tension, but the emotion itself is not "located," as it were, in the hip.

Every cell of the body contains "molecules of emotion," discovered neuroscientist Candace Pert who wrote a book of that title. Emotional memory is not just stored in the brain. Body and mind are one. Life experiences inhabit flesh and bone.

Visualizing

At the beginning of Anuttara Raja, Frankie tells us to bring our hands to our heart to set intention for practice. For instance, you might set the intention to work on breathing; on becoming calmer; on focusing more on body sensation; on staying present.

Then he tells us to bring our hands up to our third eye to visualize our intention. For me this is often a reminder to focus on my breath, and in my mind's eye I picture my belly rising with a deep breath and deflating with a full exhale.

Visualizations are another way to foster a top-down approach and are used in different ways throughout yoga practice.

"Move with feline grace," Philip will say. Even the names of the poses—Cat, Crow, Tree—encourage picturing an image in your mind.

During Savasana, people commonly report mental images. My friend Barbara has joyful hypnagogic hallucinations in Savasana.

Flights of fancy inhabit her mind as colorful images, like Ganesha, elephant-headed Hindu god of beginnings and remover of obstacles, and a popular yoga symbol.

Visualizing has profound implications for practice. Research shows visualizations and mental imagery are powerful tools for learning and improving motor control, as the brain doesn't know the difference between imagining and doing. Whether we contract our body in Cat, or visualize doing so, the same areas of the brain light up. Virtually all elite athletes use visualizations to improve performance.

To experience the power of visualization, try these suggestions. When doing Downward-Facing Dog, imagine hands and feet grounding you into the earth. When pulling knees to chest, imagine giving yourself a big hug. When doing Forward Bend, imagine all tension flowing out of your body and into the earth. When doing twists, visualize detrimental influences twisting out from your life, or twisting your body to a new, more youthful shape. Playing with these images forges the mind-body connection and wrings out self-defeating patterns.

REWIRING THE BRAIN

Both bottom-up and top-down processing during yoga class rewire the brain, a process called "neuroplasticity."

Neuroplasticity refers to how the brain and nervous system are continuously regenerating, as we gain new knowledge and experience. This happens because *neurons that fire together, wire together.* The more you engage a particular posture or pattern of thought, feeling or behavior, the stronger the network becomes.

Studies have found remarkable changes from constant use and practice of control in postures, breathing, and focused attention: increased focus and concentration; better emotional and impulse control; enhances ability to tune into your senses and be self-aware; betters decision making; greater willingness to delay gratification and more.

Think of the vestibular and proprioceptive senses as hacks into the nervous system to rewire body and mind. Studies of the brain show that the same areas and structures of the brain active in thinking, reasoning, evaluating, judging, remembering and feeling are also active during movement, in other words they are tied into vestibular and proprioceptive input. That means that whatever you think, perceive and feel while on the mat trains the brain to think, perceive and feel in those ways.

If you feel anxious or stressed during practice, the neural networks and areas of the brain responsible for the experience strengthen, while the structures that produce the experience of staying calm, optimistic, and collected weaken.

If you flip the coin and feel yoga bliss, the neural networks and areas of the brain responsible for pleasure strengthen, while the structures that produce the experience of tension, anxiety and negativity weaken.

A May 2015 study by Chantal Villemure and colleagues and published in the Frontiers in Human Neuroscience, using magnetic resonance imaging (MRI), found increased brain volume mostly in long practicing yogis. The increase was largely in the left hemisphere, the side of your brain associated with positive emotions and experiences and parasympathetic nervous system activity.

Emotions like joy and happiness have exclusively more activity in the left hemisphere of the brain when viewed with positive emission tomography (PET) brain scans, providing even more proof for yoga bliss.

The more yoga experience, the more profound were the changes in the brain. This is why so many committed yogis report extraordinary change in wellbeing. By concentrating on sensations in the body and moving purposefully, by relaxing muscles and practicing deep breathing, by thinking positive thoughts and visualizing your intention yoga powerfully facilitates positive change to break negative, self-destructive patterns and forge new ones.

This awakening of what's happening in body and mind, an awakening not shared by other low-impact activities, develops brain structures related to pro-social behavior, self-regulation, and positive thinking. As your practice deepens over time, it too becomes a strong new habit to compete with old patterns and get you to the mat.

These changes don't happen overnight. They require consistent practice and repetition as negative thinking can be stubbornly persistent. Our brain is programmed for survival and wired to perceive threat. For this reason, negative feelings are more firmly embedded in memory in the hippocampus and rule. This is why changing chronic, overlearned patterns is hard.

BDNF

Low impact activity, like yoga does something else to rewire the brain. It increases time brain-derived neurotrophic factor, or *BDNF*. This protein wires in neural connections, encourages the growth of new neurons. This happens especially in the hippocampus, fostering long-term memory, and improving mood. Depression in contrast causes the hippocampus to shrink.

Let's now look at how yoga can boost mental health.

RECAP

MINDFULNESS. Yoga teachers encourage mindfulness by encouraging one to stay present. Being mindful taps into the neocortex or thinking brain to give us some control or will power over the primal lower messages.

Catch. Cortex works up to speed only when the autonomic nervous system is dialed down to safe mode. In flight-fight, the reptilian, primitive brainstem and limbic emotional brain take over.

How Yoga Helps. Feeds the primitive brain, integrating the senses to work as a team and modulating the autonomic nervous system at the primitive level.

TOP-DOWN VS BOTTOM-UP PROCESSING. Yoga addresses the nervous system from both "bottom-up"—using the power of the body to influence the mind—and "top-down"—using the power of the mind to influence the body.

Right/Left Brain. Mind chatter takes place in the left, logical, thinking-in-words neocortex brain, and fills your head with worries and negativity. By staying present in yoga, your right, creative, intuitive brain takes over, and alpha brain waves dominate stopping negativity.

Getting in Touch with Feelings. Classes that encourage a top-down approach foster conscious awareness of feelings and intention to encourage a higher state of consciousness. By reinforcing positive behaviors, yoga gives us the tools to break thought and emotional patterns that no longer serve us.

Emotional Release. As we bend, twist and stretch muscles, we create space and expand range of motion. As we do, bodily patterns that trap emotional pain shift, unlocking repressed emotions and memories stored all over the body, and painful feelings may release.

Molecules of Emotion. Every cell of the body contains "molecules of emotion," discovered neuroscientist Candace Pert who wrote a book of that title. Emotional memory is not just stored in the brain. Body and mind are one.

Visualizing. Visualizations foster a top-down approach and are used in different ways throughout yoga practice.

REWIRING THE BRAIN. Both bottom-up and top-down processing during yoga class rewire the brain, a process called "neuroplasticity."

BDNF. Low impact activity, like yoga increases time brain-derived neurotrophic factor, or BDNF. This protein wires in neural connections, encourages the growth of new neurons.

CHAPTER 9

YOGA ON THE COUCH

"Yoga allows you to rediscover a sense of wholeness in your life, where you do not feel like you are constantly trying to fit broken pieces together."

~B.K.S. IYENGAR

D o you take little red pills for depression and little blue pills for anxiety? If so, join the crowd. Nearly 25 million adults have been taking antidepressants for at least two years, a 60% increase since 2010, while the Food and Drug Administration (FDA) estimates that over 60 million people are prescribed a type of tranquilizer every year.

If you're one of these people, consider this before you pop another pill. Low impact exercise like yoga is as effective as antidepressants for mild to moderate depression and a top anxiety buster.

When you don't want to move, do yoga. When you feel jumpy, do yoga. When you hate your body, do yoga. When you feel lonely, go to yoga class.

"The nature of yoga is to shine the light of awareness into the darkest corners of the body."

~Jason Crandell

Let's explore all the reasons why.

YOGA KEEPS YOU PRESENT

Granddaughter of author Ernest Hemingway, Mariel Hemingway grew up in a famous family haunted by depression, alcoholism, illness, and suicide. Both grandfather Ernest and sister Margaux had taken their own lives.

A holistic lifestyle has saved Mariel, with yoga at its center. "Yoga taught me how to be present in my body and showed me the healing power of moving with intention and breath," says Hemingway in an online article in Yogitimes. It helped her manage the depression that was her family curse.

The power of staying present. When depressed, you live deep inside a punishing head. Yoga forces you to focus on sensations in your body, encouraging mindfulness.

By consciously drawing awareness away from the external world and outside stimuli and directing attention internally to focus on the posture, you're less likely to veer off into the dark crevices of your mind. In this way, you can more easily avoid that mental finger wagging to admonish your insecurities: "I'm so fat. Look at all these slender yogis." "My body's so stiff. Most everyone's relaxing in lotus position." "I'm so old and wrinkled. Most of the class is in their 20's."

Teacher's mood boosting comments support greater positivity to reduce depression as well. "Don't worry how you look, only how you feel," says Philip. "Stay focused on *your* body, not on what other people around you are doing," says Elizabeth.

YOGA ENHANCES SOCIAL BONDING

Isolation often accompanies depression. In yoga class, you connect with others: through the closeness of bodies and sharing the same experience; through glances and smiles as the teacher jokes and nods and thumbs up when doing a difficult pose; through being part of a big family on a spiritual quest and feeling collective peace. Remember, the word yoga itself means union. Such connection explains in part why most are drawn more to practicing together in a yoga class than on our own.

What's going on in the brain when we feel connected to another?

Love Hormone

To start, the release of oxytocin, the love hormone in the limbic area of the brain that helps the brain tune in to subtle social cues and promotes social bonding.

Low levels of oxytocin in the brain cause social isolation and are associated with depression, anxiety, social phobia, autism, schizophrenia, post-traumatic stress disorder, anorexia nervosa, and borderline personality disorder. High levels create social bonding and the ability to tune into social cues.

Though we may touch little in yoga, the feeling of close contact and connection, of being on the same wavelength, releases oxytocin and contributes to the serenity of the practice.

Research backs this.

A 2013 study found a rise in oxytocin levels in yoga practitioners as well and social bonding. Another study found a rise in oxytocin in schizophrenics who practiced yoga.

Among the varied symptoms of schizophrenia, difficulties with social cues and relationships are particularly difficult to treat. A study from India's *National Institute of Mental Health and Neurosciences* added yoga to schizophrenia treatment. The results showed the subjects to have improved social-occupational functioning and the ability to recognize facial emotions. The improved social awareness in the yoga group was associated with increased blood levels of oxytocin.

Endocannabinois

We've talked much about what creates yoga bliss: release of happy neurotransmitters like serotonin, dopamine, oxytocin and endorphins; boosting of GABA; presence of alpha brain waves; boosting vagal tone and parasympathetic activity.

Scientists have now identified another reason for yoga bliss: the endocannabinois system (ECS). They propose that endogenous cannabinoids—the body's very own homemade marijuana—might give us a high like endorphins.

A regulatory system in the body, ECS coordinates functions of the immune, nervous and digestive systems to keep the body in balance. ECS communicates via endocannabinoids, neurotransmitters produced naturally by the body that attach to special receptors. Endocannabinoids are stimulated by oxytocins that drive the desire to connect and modulate stress and anxiety. When the brain launches a stress response, endocannibinois help put on the brakes. Researchers have found that movement produces a rise in endocannabinoids by nineteen percent.

This isn't all. When we feel good, our brain naturally produces and releases a neurotransmitter called anandamide, another cannabinoid. Similar to endorphins, anandamide reduces pain and anxiety. The more we exercise, the more the body releases anandamide. Some have speculated anandamide not endorphins might be the reason for the runner's high.

The more anandamide released, the greater the quantity of dopamine being produced. And so, during yoga practice, while the brain is producing GABA to chill us, anandamide is releasing dopamine to excite us, the two together producing the intensely euphoric state we call yoga bliss.

And the news gets even better. Anandamide stimulates brain growth in the hippocampus, sharpening memory and reducing anxiety.

Synchronized Movement

Do you move quickly in unison with the crowd when you amble down the street in midtown Manhattan? Likewise, do you loll along leisurely with the crowd when you stroll through Central Park?

Our body tends to move in rhythm with those around us. In yoga class, that means that as we breathe and move together, a mental synchronization takes place. This synchronization also adds to the feeling of being part of a big, happy family.

"I love being in a yoga class with students – 30 or 40 people all moving in unison," says Irish actor Colin Farrell.

Science concurs. Studies in which people move together, by walking, tapping, swaying or rocking together in time, report a greater sense of rapport, social support and connection.

Mirror Neurons

Giving you a deeper sense of belonging during practice in a group may come also from activating the mirror neuron system of the brain, postulates the renowned Dutch psychiatrist Bessel van der Kolk, whose work on trauma we'll discuss soon. A collection of cortical neurons, the mirror neuron system allows us to glean intention by observing the other's actions. It's related to imitation, a crucial factor for social interactions, empathy and learning.

YOGA BEATS ANTI-DEPRESSANTS

"When we are unhappy, depressed, or bored we have an easy remedy at hand: to use the body for all it's worth."

~ MIHALY CSIKSZENTMIHALY, AUTHOR OF FLOW, THE PSYCHOLOGY OF OPTIMAL EXPERIENCE

Yoga keeps the mind from brooding. It can be as effective as antidepressants in alleviating mild to moderate depression, and as effective in eliminating anxiety as anti-depressants.

Several studies support this.

In one study of 56 severely depressed people, published in *Psychosomatic Medicine* in 2000, Duke University scientists found that three 30-minute weekly workouts brought the same relief as antidepressants. And while 40 percent of those on drug treatment relapsed back into depression within six months, only 8 percent of the exercisers did.

A study from India's *National Institute of Mental Health and Neurosciences* also found that yoga helped manage depression as effectively as antidepressants in some situations. One hundred thirty-seven depressed subjects were offered three treatment options: yoga with an antidepressant, yoga alone, or an antidepressant alone. Although more than half chose the latter, 26% opted for yoga plus medication, and 17% opted for yoga alone.

Both yoga groups took part in 12 sessions over the course of a month, each led by a yoga therapist with a graduate degree in that discipline. A couple of booster sessions were provided over the next two months as well. Plus, the yoga groups were encouraged to practice daily at home.

All three treatment groups were less depressed by the study's end, but the two yoga groups were doing better than the medication alone group!

In another study, published in the *Journal of Evidence-Based Complementary & Alternative Medicine* in 2017, yoga teachers worked with clinically depressed people who responded only partially to antidepressants. The study had patients attend three Iyengar yoga classes a week over an eight-week period. Using a three-pronged approach, the classes consisted of invigorating backbends, balance-bringing inversions, and calming restoratives. The results showed a dramatic reduction in depression, so much so that the subjects would not have qualified to be in the study to begin with.

Serotonin Magic

What might account for such dramatic findings? In large part, serotonin.

Serotonin is the super depression buster. Low serotonin is associated with depression, as well as schizophrenia, drug abuse, autism, and Parkinson's disease. Anti-depressants like Prozac increase serotonin in the brain to boost mood. But so does the heavy work into joints and muscles that you get big time during yoga practice, and without side effects.

BUSTING ANGST

As you may recall, glutamate in the brain is the excitatory neurotransmitter, while GABA is the body's chill pill, quelling jumpiness and anxiety. People with depression and anxiety have low amounts of GABA in their cerebrospinal fluid.

In a ground-breaking study, researchers Streeter and colleagues compared the effects of a 12-week course of Iyengar yoga on clinical outcomes and brain GABA levels in a group of healthy volunteers and a group of people with depression and anxiety.

Included in the yoga regimen were backbends, inversions, and Savasana. Group sessions were conducted with a skilled yoga teacher, totaling three hours per week and home practice for about an hour and a half a week.

Along with Iyengar yoga, subjects practiced "coherent breathing" to raise parasympathetic tone. Coherent breathing involves breathing at the nominal rate of 6 breaths per minute with equal inhalation and exhalation.

Results showed a 27% increase in GABA levels after an hour of yoga!

If you increase GABA, you decrease excitability and therefore anxiety. If you decrease anxiety, you focus better, think more clearly and have better judgment. To no surprise the study's results suggested yoga to reduce anxiety and other negative emotions that cloud thinking.

All this happens with only a few minutes of yoga each day! So found the study. Get up in the morning and do a few sun salutations and GABA will increase in your brain and you will start your day calmer and with a clearer mind.

Contrast these findings with activating the GABA receptors in the brain with Ambien, Xanax, or a glass of wine. Though these substances will you get relaxed and sleepy, they have side effects. When they are constantly in the brain and rapidly withdrawn, you suddenly have overexcited GABA receptors. Such overexcitement can produce insomnia, anxiety, and seizures.

Another study found no significant difference in outcomes between treating stress and anxiety with yoga versus cognitive behavioral therapy (CBT). Given that CBT is the most common form of talk therapy for treating anxiety, depression, CBT and PTSD, that's huge!

Nor do you have to hit the mat daily. In one study of 65 women with depression and anxiety, the 34 women who took a yoga class twice a week for two months showed a significant decrease in depression and anxiety symptoms, compared to the 31 women who were not in the class.

These studies are only a few that support yoga's role in quelling anxiety. After reviewing several articles on yoga, Catherine Woodyard found yoga practice to inhibit the areas of the brain responsible for fear, aggression and rage. Rather, yoga stimulates the rewarding pleasure centers in the median forebrain, releasing dopamine and leading to bliss and pleasure. The result of such inhibition was lower anxiety, heart rate, respiratory rate, blood pressure, and cardiac output in students practicing yoga and meditation.

YOGA & TRAUMA

"Trauma memory is as much in the sensory receptors, in the skin and in the muscles as it is in the brain."

~ALAN FOGEL

Anyone who knows about PTSD, or post-traumatic stress disorder likely knows the name Bessel van der Kolk, internationally renowned Dutch psychiatrist and trauma specialist, and author of *The Body Keeps the Score*.

Trauma, explains van der Kolk settles into the whole body and elicits uncomfortable physical sensations, like shallow breathing and rapid heartbeat that leaves one in a constant state of anxiety. As previously discussed, yoga slows down breathing to increase heartrate variability, or vagal tone via vestibular connections, to encourage parasympathetic activity. This makes yoga an essential practice in van der Kolk's therapeutic repertoire and his studies show yoga to be equally, if not more beneficial than the best possible medications in alleviating traumatic stress symptoms.

"Yoga opens you up to feeling every aspect of your body's sensations," writes van der Kolk online in "Befriending Your Body, How Yoga Helps Heal Trauma." It provides a "gentle, safe way for people to befriend their bodies, where trauma of the past is stored...and to regain ownership of your body."

This has huge significance. Trauma victims are disconnected in mind and body. Living in a state of disassociation, they might have flashbacks to traumatic events and blank out where they can't remember. Depersonalization is common where you feel out of touch with the world around, which appears distant, like seeing through a glass darkly. By increasing body awareness, yoga helps them reconnect with self.

Along with disassociation, anxiety, hypervigilance and hypersensitivity to sound, light, touch and smell are common. Yoga asanas, breath control, and focused attention on bodily sensation modulates the nervous system to reduce hypersensitivity.

Nor is trauma rare. Through accidents, alcohol, depression, family violence, or other circumstances or events, as much as 80% of the population suffer trauma. For this reason, van der Kolk regularly gives workshops to yoga teachers to be aware of the effect of what they say and do on practitioners.

Occupational therapist Lynn Stoller couldn't agree more. The director of the Sensory-Enhanced Yoga institute and author of *Sensory-Enhanced Yoga for Self-Regulation and Trauma Healing*, Stoller trains yoga instructors, yoga therapists and others in the practice of Sensory-Enhanced yoga. Applying techniques from sensory-based occupational therapy practices, as well as recent findings from neurobiology and trauma psychology, the program serves traumatized and stressed populations, like military vets, emergency responders, victims of sexual trauma and others.

It's tricky stuff and you need much training to work with trauma victims. To start, there's no touch without permission. No loud booming music. No bright lights. No fast movement. No inversions that challenge gravity. Slow and rhythmic are your mantras.

DIGGING DEEPER

Trauma appears to impact smell. By living as if in constant danger, trauma can create strong aversion to odors, even the most benign of scents, like lavender. This is so because olfactory nerves synapse directly on the amygdala, arousing the brain into screaming "Red alert!"

I discovered this one day when I arrived to class having just dabbed lavender essential oil on my wrist. The tall red-headed woman next to me lifted her mat and moved to the other side of the room. After class, I approached her and asked why she moved. "Your lavender irritated me," she informed me. Knowing people rarely find lavender noxious without some assault to the nervous system, I asked if she had recently suffered trauma? She had, she confided. Six months earlier, she had been raped.

Lynn's passion for sensory-enhanced yoga began in 2008. At that time, Major Jon Gruel was teaching yoga during his off-duty hours as a flight instructor on the Kirkurk Air Force Base in Iraq. One day it occurred to him that yoga might reduce symptoms of combat stress, and even prevent a full-blown case of PTSD from developing.

This "aha" moment led to the Iraq Yoga Study, a randomized controlled trial of 70 deployed U.S. military personnel conducted by Lucy Cimini, founder of Yoga Warriors and Lynn Stoller as the OT Consultant. Together the two developed a treatment protocol and lesson plan for 12 older combat veterans diagnosed with PTSD and launched what would become Lynn's lifetime work to use sensory processing principle in yoga practice for trauma victims.

In 2012, Lynn and colleagues published a study in *American Journal of Occupational Therapy* in which they found sensory-enhanced hatha yoga to be effective in reducing state and trait anxiety. The results show significantly greater improvement than control participants on 16 of 18 mental health and quality-of-life factors.

Basically, sensory-enhanced yoga consists of carefully chosen sensory input to reduce the hyperarousal that accompanies PTSD: controlled breathing to coordinate movement with breath; deep touch pressure and enhanced proprioceptive input (especially from using props like bolsters and sandbags); slow rhythmic movements (no quick vinyasa flow); neutral warmth (blankets are put on the yoga student during certain asanas like Child and Savasana); and mindfulness based techniques for top-down processing. Focus is on calming forward bends, twists and forward inversions, like Downward-Facing Dog. Backbends are arousing and generally avoided.

SENSORY DEFENSIVENESS

In 2008, utilizing the treatment protocol devised by Lynn Stoller for trauma victims, occupational therapist Kimberly Mollo and her team conducted a pilot study in 2008 on the effects of Kripalu yoga on over-responsivity in the sensory defensive. The protocol included centering, warmup, an asana series of slow rhythmical movements, pranayama (used throughout the practice), final relaxation, and meditation.

The results were dramatic, showing a significant increase in cardiac baseline vagal tone, less over-responsivity and anxiety.

Mollo suggested that the enhanced proprioceptive input (heavy work) provided by the yoga increased parasympathetic nervous system activity, leading to improved feelings of well-being. At the same time, the researchers acknowledged that the pranayama techniques could have produced this effect.

SPECIAL NEEDS CHILDREN

"When describing the benefits of yoga to children, I often tell them they are like a DJ and they have a DJ's mixing board full of dials and knobs. Yoga teaches them how to adjust the volume, change channels, or add some bass. Children with difficulty processing sensory input aren't easily able to access all these knobs and dials."

~MIRA BINZEN

In 1982, yoga teacher and educator Louise Goldberg began teaching yoga at a state hospital in the Broward County Public Schools to children K-12 with emotional behavior disorders, and low functioning autism.

Since it was difficult to convey directions through language for the autistic children, who have language deficits, she relied on touch and movement, pace and rhythm, the quality of her voice and breathing.

To her astonishment, she found moments of stillness amongst the chaos. "By opening the chest," she writes in *Yoga Therapy for Children with Autism and Special Needs*, "grounding the feet and hands, deepening the breath, focusing on one point (dristi), and interacting with others naturally, I began to see children change." (p. xv).

Today, pediatric occupational therapists and some savvy educators routinely use yoga as an adjunct therapy with special needs children. This includes those with SPD, ADHD and those on the autistic spectrum, as yoga does much to enhance sensory integration.

By learning how to tune into their bodies and sensations (interoceptive awareness), they achieve better body awareness. By building strength, core, balance and flexibility, they achieve better coordinated movement. By having the poses broken down into their smallest components, their motor planning improves. By learning how to focus and concentrate in the poses, they become better able to learn.

The poses also help them to become better modulated. Typically, special needs children will avoid sensation, overly seek it, or see-saw between the two; avoiding some sensation, like touch, while seeking other sensation, like movement, (the autistic child spinning endlessly).

For kids who experience sensory overload, some yoga poses, like Child Pose and Savasana, encourage sensory withdrawal, quieting the nervous system, as does practicing with eyes closed to shut out sensory stimulation. Staying still in a pose offers also a break from sensory overload.

For kids who seek sensation, heavy work into the joints and muscles through balancing poses, or core strengthening poses like plank dampens their seeking behavior (running around, clowning, and so on) by releasing serotonin, the feel good transmitter, and inhibiting dopamine, the reward.

Let's now look closely at how specific poses during practice boosts our primary senses.

RECAP

HOW YOGA HELPS ALLEVIATE DEPRESSION

Keeps You Present. By consciously drawing awareness away from the external world and outside stimuli and directing attention internally to focus on the posture, you're less likely to veer off into the dark crevices of your mind.

Yoga Enhances Social Bonding. Isolation often accompanies depression. In yoga class, you connect with others through:

- closeness of bodies and sharing the same experience;

- glances and smiles as the teacher jokes and nods and thumbs up when doing a difficult pose;

- being part of a big family on a spiritual quest and feeling collective peace.

WHAT'S GOING ON IN THE BRAIN WHEN WE FEEL CONNECTED

Love Hormone. In yoga, the feeling of close contact and connection, of being on the same wavelength, releases oxytocin and contributes to the serenity of the practice.

Endocannabinois. Another reason for yoga bliss is the endocannabinois system (ECS), which is the body's homemade marijuana. Researchers have found that movement produces a rise in endocannabinoids by nineteen percent.

Synchronized Movement. Our body tends to move in rhythm with those around us. In yoga class, that means that as we breathe and move together, a mental synchronization takes place.

Mirror Neurons. Giving you a deeper sense of belonging during practice in a group may come also from activating the mirror neuron system of the brain. A collection of cortical neurons, the mirror neuron system allows us to glean intention by observing the other's actions.

YOGA BEATS ANTI-DEPRESSANTS. Yoga keeps the mind from brooding. It can be as effective as antidepressants in alleviating mild to moderate depression, and as effective in eliminating anxiety as anti-depressants.

Serotonin Magic. Serotonin, released in droves during intense yoga practice is the super depression buster.

Busting Angst. People with depression and anxiety have low amounts of GABA in their cerebrospinal fluid. Yoga practice boosts GABA.

Trauma. Studies show yoga to be equally, if not more beneficial than the best possible medications in alleviating traumatic stress symptoms.

SENSORY DEFENSIVENESS. Research has shown yoga to reduce hypersensitivity by increasing vagal tone and parasympathetic nervous system activity.

SPECIAL NEEDS CHILDREN. Pediatric occupational therapists and some savvy educators routinely use yoga as an adjunct therapy with special needs children, including those with SPD, ADHD and those on the autistic spectrum.

- By learning how to tune into their bodies and sensations (interoceptive awareness), they achieve better body awareness.

- By building strength, core, balance and flexibility, they achieve better coordinated movement.

- By having the poses broken down into their smallest components, their motor planning improves.

- By learning how to focus and concentrate in the poses, they become better able to learn.

PART III
THE PRACTICE

"Follow your bliss."

~Joseph Campbell

CHAPTER 10

SENSATIONAL POSES

"My Body Is My Temple and Asanas Are My Prayers"

~B.K.S. IYENGAR

My yoga journey began in my 30's with a basic hatha class. At that time, I was studying jazz dance. Compared to dance, the yoga was slow and boring. I took only a few classes.

In my 40's, I moved to Florida and joined a fitness center that offered Bikram yoga. It was strenuous and challenging. I loved it and practiced Bikram three to four times a week for three or four years until I began to practice Power Vinyasa yoga.

Today, when schedule permits, I typically do Vinyasa two to three days a week, Anuttara Raja four to five days, and either Kundalini or Iyengar once a week as well. Each practice has something different to offer—all valuable.

From Vinyasa to Bikram to Iyengar to Kundalini to a basic hatha yoga class, different styles of yoga exist with different philosophies, different poses and sequences. They vary from slow and mellow to fast and charged, depending on the level of the students.

Regardless of yoga style, all tend to follow a general pattern. Combining awareness of body alignment with breathing and movement, the class begins slowly with basic asanas or postures to warm up the body and gradually introduces more challenging poses. The last half hour will consist typically of poses to wind down and the class ends in Savasana.

In most classes, you move through a series of poses divided equally for strength, flexibility, and balance. The routine will typically be structured so that each pose counterbalances preceding one, stretching and strengthening. For instance, Tree Pose for strengthening might be followed by Side Bend or Forward Bend for stretching.

Some asanas are easy, like Mountain, Child and Forward Bend, and you barely sweat. These poses involve moderate proprioceptive and vestibular input. Others build strength and endurance, like inversions and one-legged balance poses and the sweat pours down. These poses give you a proprioceptive and vestibular "pow."

Vinyasa

According to a US survey of 10,000 people by DOYOUYOGA, 57% of yogis, or more than half practice Vinyasa. It's the style I've been practicing the longest.

The primary poses that comprise the practice, such as the Sun Salutation sequence, the Warrior poses, and other poses like triangle are common in most forms of yoga.

Let's explore a sequence that exemplifies Vinyasa practice.

Vinyasa sequence

Class opens with warm up asanas, like Child, Easy Pose, Mountain or Forward Bend. How many and what kind will vary depending on level of class. In a basic class, you will a slower opening and you may do some head and shoulder warm-ups in Easy Pose, for instance, along with some seated twists.

After a basic warm up in Vinyasa, several Sun Salutations (Surya Namaskar) typically follow. They start with Surya Namaskar A and, depending on level of class, will be followed by a few B and C sequences. Basic classes might offer only A, while more advanced classes may offer all three. Other classes, like Iyengar and Kundalini may use some or all of the poses in Sun Salutation but not in a flowing sequence, while Bikram will use only a few of the poses.

Sun Salutations A & B
Surya Namaskara A & B

One day recently in Power Vinyasa, I had a special treat. In front of me was Christina, a dark-haired, tall, slender, long-legged former ballet dancer with the Boca Raton Ballet company. Her movements were exquisitely fluid, her body super flexible and graceful. Generally I keep my eyes closed as I practice. That day I kept them wide open, as I stared, dazzled at the lithe, supple movement of her body flowing through a Sun Salutation. Because of the fluid flow, Sun Salutations are the closest thing yoga comes to dance movement and it's not unusual to find dancers practicing.

The Sun Salutation is the signature sequence of Vinyasa flow. And for good reason. Moving through a Sun Salutation eases you into moving, centers and grounds you in the present, strengthens and tones all muscles of the body and lubricates the joints.

It moves you into the breath as you inhale and exhale coordinated with the flow of the poses and builds internal heat to warm up the body.

As you flow through the sequence, you get enhanced proprioceptive input throughout the torso and all four limbs. This comprehensive activation happens through extension and flexion of the trunk (extension in Downward-Facing-Dog; flexion up in Upward-Facing-Dog for instance); slow rhythmical vestibular input from continual head change while moving up and down, forward and backward; deep touch pressure as palms and feet push into the ground.

Vinyasa as Transition

As you move in and out of strengthening, balancing and inversion poses throughout the rest of a Vinyasa class, you'll take a "Vinyasa," or modified Sun Salutation often. It consists of Upward-Facing-Dog and Downward-Facing Dog as a transition between poses. This helps to refocus, realign, and bring awareness back to your body during a challenging practice.

Let's break down some common poses within a Sun Salutation for their sensory properties.

MOUNTAIN POSE (TADASANA)

(Sharon)

I'm in awe of people who sit up straight at their computer. I slump. With lordosis, scoliosis and two fused vertebrae, sitting up straight creates muscle tension. In the Mountain pose, though I'm in perfect alignment: erect spine and arms pulled back and down; feet together and weight evenly distributed; head slightly tilted forward and chin lowered.

Of course I have constant reminders. "Notice if your head is aligned directly over your torso," says James.

Feeling tall and grounded in this pose, I relax and become aware of my posture.

A standard and easy pose used in virtually every yoga style, Mountain is the first pose in Vinyasa and involves keeping the body straight and still. A good exercise in body awareness (and muscle control), it will be repeated throughout the practice to rest, to reset, and as a transition.

In times of stress, it's a good stance to assume as you will automatically take in a full, three-dimensional breath, and feel your whole torso expand.

FORWARD BEND (UTTANASANA)

(Sharon)

A common pose in different styles of yoga, Forward Bend is easy for me and one of my favorites. After years of yoga, my hamstrings are stretched out and even first thing in the morning I can easily bend forward and place my hands flat on the ground aside my feet.

During Forward Bend, the back of your whole body is stretching: calf muscles, thighs, buttocks, and back muscles. At the front of your body, your muscles work to stabilize you in the deep bend, especially in legs.

With the head down, bending forward lengthens the spine, stretches the back muscles, and increases oxygen to the brain. Stimulating the vestibular system, Forward Bend Pose engages the parasympathetic system, relaxing and calming you.

Though simple to do, the pose creates muscle activation to increase body awareness. Active inner and outer hamstrings create tension at the back of the knee that help make you more aware of your knee; active deep fibers of the gluteus maximus encourage sensing of the back of the upper part of the femur, while muscle activation at the back of the thigh and hip puts you in touch with your thigh and hip bone.

BASIC BENEFITS:

Vestibular: Head down stimulates the vestibular receptors.

Proprioceptive: Moderate extension.

Body Awareness: Through muscle activation and control.

Breath: Encourages deep exhalation.

DOWNWARD-FACING-DOG (ADHO MUKHA SVANASANA)

(Marjorie)

Basic to most Yoga classes, Downward-Facing-Dog has become as synonymous with yoga as plié to ballet. In this iconic pose, you use the entire body, strengthening and stretching almost every muscle and feeling its effects from head to toe. Home base, Downward-Facing Dog is the pose you flow into and out of, often until Savasana.

I confess to not loving Downward-Facing Dog. Though it looks easy, it requires great concentration to do it correctly and get the full benefit. Recently in class, James pulled my hips back when I was in the pose. My whole body extended as if I were in traction. This is how the pose is supposed to feel. Since then, I've made more of an attempt to regain that feeling on my own.

There's another issue. For years I let my swayback fall during the posture, increasing my arc. In Iyengar, I learned to keep my back slightly curved inward by consciously pulling in my ribcage and stomach muscles to use core.

Still, at times I neglect core and fall back into an arc. Recently, my teacher Elizabeth gently grabbed my hips and firmly pulled me backward to straighten out my spine. Hmmm. Simple.

Since her adjustment, I now consciously draw my tailbone underneath my pelvis, so my back isn't swaying and my tushy protruding. I pull my rib cage back, and drop my shoulders, *most of the time.* When I do, my back straightens out.

Without conscious awareness of what the body is doing— without body awareness—Downward-Facing Dog is challenging. With body awareness, you focus on the correct way to do the pose and in time, you automatically spread fingers, push heels down, suck up stomach to the spine—core, core core—pull the hips back and extend the body as if in traction and reap the benefits. That only took 25 years of practice!

BASIC BENEFITS:

Vestibular: Inverted head challenges balance.

Proprioceptive: Extension in whole body; flexion in ankles and wrists; pressure on arms; weight bearing in hands, wrists, elbows, knees, ankles and feet, all sending information to the brain about where the body is in space.

Body Awareness: Extra weight placed on the arms fosters enhances awareness of your body.

Tactile: Deep pressure into hands and feet.

Strength: Stronger hands, wrists, low back, hamstrings, calves and Achilles tendon.   Posture: Opens anterior chest wall and shoulders.

Bilateral Coordination: Requires using both sides of body evenly.

Breathing: Deepens respiration.

UPWARD-FACING-DOG (Urdhva Mukha Svanasana)

(Gerry)

Upward-Facing-Dog flexes the back into a backbend. Beginners, those with back issues, and seniors often have poor range of motion and in a backbend barely bend back at all.

The more you hit the mat the suppler your back becomes. Years of yoga have kept my back reasonably flexible despite my back issues, and in a backbend, I still have some curve to my spine. Given that I spend hours a day typing away at the computer, this helps counteract some of my hunching.

A massive front body opener, Upward-Facing-Dog stretches chest and spine, while strengthening wrists, arms, and shoulders. Where else outside of a yoga studio do you open your body in the *opposite* range of motion?

While a basic backbend pose, Upward-Facing-Dog is nevertheless challenging as it requires much arm and upper body strength. It also requires the use of Uddiyana Banda, as you suck in the belly button and lift it as you move your body upward.

As a Vinyasa class progresses, backbends will become more extreme, offering greater flexion and extension. Examples are the Mermaid, as in the photo, and Bridge, poses that are done in more advanced classes in the latter half of the class, after the body is sufficiently warmed up.

(Marissa)

Backbends are especially energizing for those with low muscle tone, helping to strengthen lower back and buttocks.

(Ryan)

BASIC BENEFITS:

Vestibular: Vertical resistance against gravity.

Proprioceptive: Flexion into wrists, elbows and shoulders; extension into arms, knees and ankles, extending body from head to toe; weight bearing through both arms. Increases back flexibility.

Tactile: Palms pressing down into the ground provides deep pressure into palms along with energy and awareness in raising arms.

Core: Works core.

Muscle Control: Requires much arm and upper body strength, strengthening spine, gluteal muscles, thighs, arms and shoulders.

Strength: Improves whole body strength and builds shoulder stability.

Breathing: Supports fuller breathing.

Posture: Proper alignment of head, spine, arms, shoulders, lower back, legs and feet to improve posture creates space and openness in front of body and strength in back of body.

Bilateral Coordination: Uses both arms at same time to increase ability to coordinate bilateral integration.

Emotional: Opens chest to elevate mood, reducing tendency to curl into body when depressed or overwhelmed. At a cellular level, when you practice a backbend, endorphins in the brain circulate in the blood, and send a signal to every cell that you're happy.

PLANK

(Jen)

A basic, somewhat challenging full body exercise, plank involves much muscle engagement and strength. I can still manage the pose easily enough. That is unless we hold it for longer than 10 seconds or so as it involves stronger core than I have at this point in my life and I shimmy and count the seconds.

Plank is used not only as part of Sun Salutation but throughout the practice as a transition pose.

BASIC BENEFITS:

Vestibular: Challenges balance.

Proprioceptive: Engages many muscles to keep the body in position, especially core muscles; offers weight bearing through a flat palm and strengthens muscles of the hand.

Tactile: Deep pressure in hands.

Muscle Control: Requires contracting all muscles in body.

Body Awareness: Heavy muscle engagement creates high levels of tension and builds body awareness.

Core: Requires total body engagement, emphasizing core and hip stability; help develop isometric strength in core muscles to help keep from hunching while standing or sitting for long periods of time.

Posture: Strengthens back, chest, shoulders, neck, and abs to make it easier to keep shoulders back and lower back in a neutral position while sitting or standing — two vital components of good posture.

WARRIOR POSES

WARRIOR I

(Gerry)

WARRIOR II

(Anna Maria)

WARRIOR III

(Jen)

When I first began yoga practice in my 40's, I prided myself on my flexibility in getting deeply into the Warrior poses. Front foot bent deeply at 90 degrees, back leg straight, weight properly into the arch in Warrior II.

Now, in my 70's, my body doesn't have the same deep extension as it did in my 40's. Still, when I glance in the mirror in Warrior II, I see my hands outstretched, as if pulled by an invisible rope. It feels great. I'm youthing!

Warrior I, II, and III are some of the most common postures in yoga practice. And for good reason. Less intimidating than more advanced postures, they're approachable for most bodies, while building strength, confidence, and waking up the body to encourage body awareness. Sun Salutation C adds Warrior I, while Warrior II and III will typically follow the Sun Salutation sequence.

While Sun Salutations explore the Sagittal Plane (flexion and extension), Warrior II explores the Coronal Plane (abducting or moving away from the midline and adducting or moving toward the midline), as does Triangle and Wide Legged Forward Folds that typically take place later in class.

Warrior I and II can be practiced by most, while Warrior III is for the intermediate and advanced level.

BASIC BENEFITS:

Vestibular: Improves balance by standing asymmetrically in Warrior I and II. In Warrior III, body's center of gravity over the foundation builds balance as the body works hard to remain still and upright.

Proprioceptive: Improves balance and stability. Movement of legs and arms in various directions enhances spatial orientation, fostering coordination. Warrior III provides weight bearing on standing leg and adds extension with traction.

Body Awareness: Aligns and grounds body; makes you aware of internal rotation of back foot in Warrior I and II, and squaring of hips and full plant of back foot in Warrior I. All require great perception of where body is in space. "Keep reaching. Keep lengthening," says James to encourage body awareness in Warrior I pose (Virabhadrasana A).

Tactile: Deep pressure into the feet.

Core: Employs bandhas and builds core muscles.

Muscle Strength & Control: Strengthens legs and ankles; builds core muscles. Warrior III engages all core muscles.

Bilateral Integration: Using both sides of body promotes coordination to easily get into and manage the pose.

Mental: Helps train the mind to stay present and focused. Enhances self-esteem as the poses are challenging. And they require endurance to hold poses for a length of time to work on balance and muscular strength.

Muscle Control: Strengthens feet, hamstrings, quadriceps, and gluteus, to build core power.

Breath: Warrior II opens chest and shoulders, improving breathing capacity and increasing circulation throughout the body.

Other: All the Warriors poses improve circulation and respiration and energize the entire body.

ILLUMINATING

A 2010 Harvard Study on "power posing," like Warrior I & II showed that holding open-body postures for two minutes decreases cortisol and increases testosterone, a confidence-boosting hormone, for less anxiety and more self-assuredness.

ANTI-GRAVITY

We've talked much about how yoga asanas capture the full span of the different elements of vestibular input—from defying gravity in poses such as the Boat, The Bow, Bridge, Cobra, Side Plank, and Wheel to extreme inversions like shoulder stand headstand and handstand to subtler ways, like creating an arc, bending forward and backward and moving on the diagonal.

Let's explore how different yoga poses detect and process different planes and directions of movement: back and forth, side to side, rotary, diagonal, and vertical input.

Back and Forth

As I move through a Vinyasa, I revel in the feel of my body moving back and forth, almost like a dance. Such linear movement calms and inhibits the reticular activating system via the vestibular system.

Side to Side

I'm a rhythm fanatic. Once I start moving side to side, I don't want to stop. I love Kundalini yoga for this reason.

Moving rhythmically constitutes much of Kundalini yoga practice. Most classes start seated, as you move side to side slowly and gradually pickup speed. Breath is coordinated with movement: inhale to the right; exhale to the left.

Diagonal

Moving on the diagonal or side-stretching lengthens the muscles between the ribs and pelvis, including parts of the low back. This opens the sides of the rib cage, improving rib cage mobility and the expansiveness of the lungs. This makes breathing easier.

(Heidi)

Rotation

Ah the joy of childhood, spinning around on the merry-go-round and whiling around like dervishes.

Spinning is a powerful means of vestibular sensation. Rarely is it done in a yoga class, though I've had a few classes throughout the years where teachers have thrown it in.

In yoga, we get some rotary movement in twists.

(Jen)

Twisting keeps the spine flexible and releases tension in the gut. This has a great calming effect because 90% of serotonin, our happy hormone is made in the digestive tract. This is why tension, anxiety and stress tend to be accompanied by tummy aches, gas, bloating, constipation or diarrhea.

The vagus nerve passes through the digestive tract. When you exhale, you trigger parasympathetic arousal, the relaxation response. Twisting improves exhalation by optimizing the internal intercostals and the abdominals, the respiratory apparatus involved in exhalation. Similarly, forward bends improve exhalation and calm the nervous system. At home, I set up my system in the morning by taking several full breaths in forward bend.

In my Anuttara Raja class, we do many twists, or axial rotation of the spine, compressing muscles and lubricating the spine to increase range of motion. The studio has a mirror on three sides and we are encouraged to look in the mirror. When I do, I smile: my twisted body looks youthful.

While I don't have the same range of motion as I did thirty years ago, I beat others in the class my age by a mile, whose bodies are barely turned. Thank you, yoga.

Inversions

My Power Vinyasa yoga class is three-fourths over and I'm already in the zone.

"Time for handstands," says James.

Great. Handstands against the wall mean a huge vestibular whollop, along with rich proprioceptive and deep pressure input.

Most of the class lifts their bodies onto the wall easily, raising one leg and then, using core, bringing the other leg up with control.

(Yoga South)

A few super yogis with amazing core lift up, one leg at a time, in the middle of the floor.

I don't have the core to control bringing one leg at a time onto the wall. Standing a few feet away from the wall, I fly up all at once, sometimes needing two or three tries until I can stabilize my body against the wall.

But I get there—most of the time. With all that intense proprioceptive input at once into my hands, wrists, shoulders, and hips, as well as the balance receptors in my inner ear going to town with my head upside down, I'm flying when I come down, energized and alive. That I can still do one at my age empowers me.

To do the pose correctly and with the most muscle engagement requires using both *Mula Bandha* and *Uddiyana Bandha* big time or you'll look like a banana and experience back pain. When I focus on lifting the floor of the pelvis (basically doing a Kegel) and on contracting my upper abdomen, I stay up there longer. When I get down, my body thrums with both peaceful energy and enthusiastic serenity that lasts for a few hours. If I skip this inversion, as I often do because of tendinitis in my wrists, I don't go as deeply into the zone.

Inverted postures like shoulder, head, and hand stands provide traction and intense joint compression. They flood the brain with freshly oxygenated blood and relax the heart by allowing blood to flow to the upper body, improving circulation and enhancing energy. By stimulating the brain and increasing blood supply, they improve memory as well.

In addition to a powerful dose of vestibular input, inversions give you lots of heavy work into the joints to provide the most bang for your workout buck. The two together are profoundly regulating and organizing. Recall that the proprioceptive sense is the grand modulator, releasing serotonin to calm you when you are excited and alert you when you are lethargic. When you come down from inversion poses, you feel clearer and calmer.

In yoga practice, inversions refer to any pose where the head is above the heart, and range from child and Downward-Facing-Dog to advanced poses, like Feathered Peacock and Handstand.

Basic

Child (Balasana)

(Yoga South)

The go-to pose when marching up to overload or exhaustion, Child pose offers many benefits:

Vestibular: Head is downward.

Proprioception: Back flexion.

Relaxation: Relaxes back after extensions; soothing pressure of folded limbs triggers PNS.

Eyes: Deep flexion with ocular pressure; eyes shut for sensory withdrawal and to focus inward.

Breath: Allows sensation of breathing deeply.

Legs Up Wall

(Jen)

A restorative pose, Legs Up Wall is profoundly relaxing. Often, my Iyengar class will end in Legs Up Wall, with a sandbag across chest or lower abdomen to increase deep pressure, or legs up on a chair for a simple inversion during Savasana.

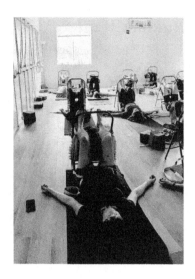

(Iyengar at Iyoga)

More Advanced

Handstand

(Alexis)

Headstand Against Wall

(Yoga South)

Headstand

(Jen)

This is one pose I never do. No one who ever had head trauma should compress their head.

Shoulder Stand

(Jen)

Modifications for Every Body

Difficult inversions take much strength and core. In an Iyengar yoga class, modifications are done routinely using props. This allows anyone, including the elderly to get into a pose.

These props in turn add deep pressure tactile sensation to further release feel good, organizing chemical.

Here are some examples from Iyengar yoga.

Headstand Supported

(Stephanie)

Shoulderstand Supported

(Iyoga Iyengar Studio)

Let's now explore ways to increase sensory power during practice.

RECAP

COMMON POSES & BENEFITS

MOUNTAIN POSE. A standard and easy pose used in virtually every yoga style, Mountain is the first pose in Vinyasa and involves keeping the body straight and still. A good exercise in body awareness (and muscle control), it will be repeated throughout the practice to rest, to reset, and as a transition.

FORWARD BEND. A common pose in different styles of yoga, Forward Bend has many benefits including stretching the back of the whole body, stabilizing the muscles, lengthening the spine and increasing oxygen to the brain.

DOWNWARD-FACING-DOG. In this pose, you use the entire body, strengthening and stretching almost every muscle and feeling its effects from head to toe.

UPWARD-FACING-DOG. A massive front body opener, Upward-Facing-Dog stretches chest and spine, while strengthening wrists, arms, and shoulders.

PLANK. A basic, somewhat challenging full body exercise, plank involves much muscle engagement and strength.

WARRIOR POSES. Warrior I, II, and III are some of the most common postures in yoga practice. Less intimidating than more advanced postures, they're approachable for most bodies, while building strength, confidence, and waking up the body to encourage body awareness.

ANTI-GRAVITY POSES. Different yoga poses detect and process different planes and directions of movement: back and forth, side to side, rotary, diagonal, and vertical input.

Inversions. Inverted postures provide traction and intense joint compression and flood the brain with oxygen. In yoga practice, inversions refer to any pose where the head is above the heart, and range from child and Downward-Facing-Dog to advanced poses, like Feathered Peacock, Headstand, and Handstand.

Modifications for Every Body. Difficult inversions take much strength and core. In an Iyengar yoga class, modifications are done routinely using props. This allows anyone, including the elderly to get into a pose.

CHAPTER 11

ENHANCING SENSORY POWER

"The brain needs lots of information and that information comes from the senses."

~WINNIE DUNN, LIVING SENSATIONALLY

F or my age, my balance is good. I can stay in Tree and, on good days, in Eagle for a time. Still, I waver in many standing poses like Warrior III.

Could I make it better?

Eager to find out, I attended Elizabeth's Strong Yoga class using the Strongboard balancing board.

(Elizabeth)

(Elizabeth)

As they write on their website, The StrongBoard Balance® utilizes MULTI SPRING TECHNOLOGY™ that works with your body to deliver the perfect amount of stimulation to keep your core musculature and stabilizing muscles engaged and contracted, while training your central nervous system, improving posture, proprioception and reaction time.

Elizabeth has you doing a modified Vinyasa class using the Strongboard. Some poses are done standing on the board, like Forward Bend, Fierce Pose, and Warrior III while others are done with hands, or body on the board and legs off, like Upward-Facing-Dog and Downward-Facing Dog, Warrior I and II, and Triangle. All require strength, core and a steady body.

Oh my. Could I manage this?

I got on the board and wavered side to side as if on a boat in choppy water.

"Today just concentrate on standing on the board until you get used to the imbalance," Elizabeth told me, placing a chair in front of me should I become too unsteady and fall off.

The first few moments I wavered uncomfortably and gripped the chair. But within 10 minutes or so of trying to stabilize my body on the Board, I wavered only slightly. Amazingly I found I could do a few basic poses on the StrongBoard, like Forward Bend and even lift up each foot slightly, all without falling off. I kept the chair in front of me but, throughout the rest of the class used it less and less for support. By the third class, I was able to balance with one leg pulled into my chest.

Various props and other ways to enhance sensory input into yoga practice exist.

The more you utilize these different ancillary tools, the stronger the sensory input and, ultimately, your yoga practice.

Let's look at ways to enhance sensory input in practice.

ENHANCING BALANCE

How good is your balance? Here's a test. Stand with feet hip width apart. Close your eyes and lift one leg.

Did you wobble? No problem. Balance encompasses vestibular, proprioceptive and visual input. Yoga practice trains and improves all: vestibular with all the head changes; proprioception with all the push and pull involved in the asanas; and visual input through focus and dristi.

In addition to using the Strongboard, here are ways to enhance balance in yoga practice.

Remove Support

In Power Vinyasa yoga, James will suggest lifting your hand from the ground or block in poses such as half-moon. Adjusting me, he has lifted my hand so fingers only are touching the ground. With effort, I'm able to balance briefly.

Several poses offer the opportunity for lifting a hand or a leg up. In Cat/Cow, you can lift one leg and pull it forward, for instance, or to the side.

Vary the Surface You Balance On

Occasionally, I attend a sundown class on the beach. While watching the red sun as it disappears beyond the horizon as we flow through Downward-Facing Dog, Upward-Facing-Dog and Plank Pose is delightful, balancing on an unsteady surface like sand or grass is more of a challenge than on a stable surface. Maintaining balance requires more strength, and you need to develop an "earthy" feel for the surface.

In fact, just being outside where the clouds are moving above or next to a body of water where the water is rippling beyond your gaze presents a challenge for balance. Your peripheral and central systems will conflict with one another as they try to provide you with a sense of true upright.

Still, challenging balance with different surfaces has benefits. Instability on a surface prevents you from wedging your body into postures, putting pressure in knees, hips, elbows, and shoulders.

Hang Like a Bat

Hanging upside down is the quickest way to get quick, intense and long lasting vestibular input.

Many props exist to help you hang freely like Batman.

Yoga hanging wall: This is a sling attached to the wall that makes it easy to get in out of postures. We have one at my yoga studio (see photo) and I love to use it to fortify my practice.

(SJ)

Yoga headstand bench: This allows you to do a headstand without your head touching the floor. It requires some core to get into a headstand and stay there and may be initially difficult if you have low muscle tone and little musculature.

I have one at home and use it often. Though it's a bit uncomfortable on the shoulders, it's the only way I can do a headstand as I cannot compress my head because of my past head trauma.

TAKE HEED

If you get dizzy doing an inversion, go slowly and build up the time you need to stay in them.

Remove or Change Vision

Once you are comfortable in a balance pose with eyes open, you can challenge your balance by trying the pose with eyes closed. One pose in which I attempt this is Half Moon, though I will waver.

Closing the eyes in a pose helps improve proprioception as well as the vestibular sense, as you have to rely on your internal sense of where you are in space to balance.

You can also keep eyes open but change head position, by looking up, looking down, looking side to side or turning head.

Visualize

In Tree Pose imagine that the foot you are balanced on is the root of the tree and the leg is the trunk, while the head and outstretched arms are the branches and leaves of the tree.

By visualizing, you will likely find you can concentrate better and hold the pose longer. By holding the pose longer, you increase body awareness, particularly in the sole of the standing foot.

Buy a Better Mat

For years I bought the cheapest yoga mat to save money. Invariably I had to replace it every six months or so.

Since most people in my Power Vinyasa yoga class were using a Manduka mat, I laid out the $100 knowing it was long lasting. What a difference! Dense cushioning for better support and stability allowed me to get deeper into the poses and it was softer on the joints. Better grip for my feet also improved balance.

ENHANCING BODY AWARENESS

After placing my mat on the floor in Iyengar class, I saunter over to the wall to gather my props: a couple of blankets, a few blocks, a strap. Later, towards the end of class, I'll get a sandbag for restorative poses.

Props define Iyengar yoga. They help you to perform the asanas correctly and minimize the risk of injury or strain.

They do something else, as well. Props such as blocks or sandbags provide deeper input into joints and muscles, enhancing kinesthetic awareness of what your body's doing and fostering body awareness.

Sandbags

I'm lying on the floor in Savasana at the end of Anuttara Raja. I know we'll lie there for at least five minutes. I place a sandbag across my chest. My breathing slows more. A surge of energy that some call "chi" or life force pulses through my veins from my shoulder to my fingertips, intensifying the comfort tenfold. The deep pressure of the hug enfolds me.

Teachers can't be everywhere pressing down on you. A sandbag proves a useful alternative.

The weight of the sandbag anchors you down, intensifying deep pressure. With deeper pressure you realize greater awareness in the body through increased sensory input across a large surface area. As you surrender, you absorb the benefits of practice more fully, intensifying the calming relaxation in the pose.

You can place the sandbag on knees during seated poses or on thigh in a kneeling pose. In Child Pose, you can place a sandbag on your sacrum. As you breathe deeply, you will feel gentle traction in low back. In Legs Up the Wall, you can place a sandbag across your groin and in Sleeping Serpent, across your upper back.

Blocks

Yoga blocks are standard in yoga class. They provide the stability and balance needed to encourage optimal alignment, to get you deeper into poses, and, therefore, increase strength and flexibility.

Blocks come in many materials, from squishy foam to wood; each with unique benefits. If you put hands or feet on a foam block, the unstable surface causes the proprioceptors in hands and feet to fire constantly. This forces your nervous system to adapt to each instantaneous movement.

In Elizabeth's StrongYoga class, we place a block between the inner thighs while on the StrongBoard in poses such as Forward Bend and Chair Pose. Squeezing into the block activates the inner thighs and energizes the pose, providing deep pressure touch. This gives you tactile information to help maintain hip, knee and ankle alignment.

Blocks between the legs are standard in Iyengar.

Other Props

Strap

I'm lying on my back, legs up pointing to the ceiling. Elizabeth tells us to lower the left leg and pull the straight, vertical right leg toward us. I do. She comes by and places a strap across the instep of my vertical right foot. I grab the two ends. She tells me to pull the strap down and pull my leg forward toward my head slightly without disrupting the pull into my hips. Ohhh. What a difference. Much more input into my hips.

Iyengar created the strap as part of his classes in the early 1970s. It's remained a useful prop in yoga particularly to assist in poses that require you to bind.

(Iyengar at IYoga)

Add a strap to Dancer's Pose and you enhance the pulling and extension for more proprioception.

(Elizabeth on StrongBoard)

Balls

More and more yoga teachers are using different balls in their classes to help you sink deeper into a stretch or massage away tension held in your connective tissue. This enhances proprioception.

In teaching yin classes at Yoga South, Tammy used a spikey red ball as a foot massage at the beginning of class. I bought one and use it to massage my feet before starting class.

During my Anuttara Yoga class, I use the black balls from Yamuna's Body Rolling ™ on different parts of my body.

For instance, when lying on my belly in Sleeping Serpent, I place one ball into each hip socket between pelvis and floor. This provides a deep myofascial massage during the three to four minutes we're in the pose.

Eye Pillow

Eye pillows during Savasana provide comforting pressure to the muscles around the eyes, causing them to soften and release. If, like me, you spend hours a day at the computer, eye pillows can help release some of the resultant eye strain.

Hammock

As mentioned previously, with your body in hanging in space, you feel muscles and connective tissue more strongly, enhancing body awareness.

ENHANCING TACTILE SENSATION

Many ways exist to enhance tactile sensation and deep pressure touch during yoga practice.

Let's explore different opportunities.

Use Greater Force

I'm in Easy Pose in Kundalini yoga. Monica, the teacher says, "Push your finger digits together in prayer, lower your head, take in a deep breath and expel the breath through your mouth slowly until all air is out of your lungs." We do this for two full minutes while Monica keeps repeating, "Push your finger pad tight. Push! This is the key to the pose."

Opportunities exist in several poses to push more into hands and feet and deepen pressure. In Tree Pose, you can push your foot more into your upper inner thigh; in Cat/Cow, you can push your hands more forcefully into the ground.

Use Wall

During Iyenger, I'm bent into Standing Forward Bend, my back leaning into the wall. With the wall flattening my pack and pushing into me, I feel my spine elongate and my neck flatten. I am able to get deeper into my backbend and enhance skin sensation. Afterwards, my spine erect and strong, a new energy flows through me. Life feels great.

While different styles utilize the wall occasionally, in Iyengar the wall as prop is an essential part of practice.

The wall enables you to hold, lift, or suspend a part of your body during postures; poses are deeper with greater stability and can be held longer giving you greater input into joints and muscles. You get more deep pressure into hands and feet, as well as the back, when flattening your back against the wall in poses such as Forward Bend or Chair Pose.

(Jen)

By providing an entity to literally to lean on, the wall also confers a greater feeling of psychological support.

Use Ropes

In an Iyengar class, ropes attach to the wall as another prop. With the use of gravity as a natural form of resistance, the body opens further than in regular yoga practice, adding push and pull into the joints

(IYoga)

(IYoga)

Try Partner Yoga

At my first stab at partner yoga, I did a handstand onto my partner's back. She grabbed my legs and swaddled them over her shoulders so I could hang freely. It was euphoric and energizing. I never wanted to come down. For a week, I drove my boyfriend crazy with my request to turn around so I could fly onto his back.

Partner yoga takes on different forms, from two people leaning, pushing or pulling each other, to a group engaging in mutually supportive fun, as the photo shows.

(Yoga South)

Fly Through the Air

Full body deep pressure touch is ongoing during aerial yoga as your body pushes into the hammock. Floating above the ground during Savasana, completely cocooned in the silk in the fetal tuck creates full flexion of the body and deep pressure along the whole back body to create a euphoric, relaxing experience to end each practice.

If you are close enough to the wall to push it, you can swing gently side to side, adding a dose of vestibular input. In the fetal tuck, swinging, deep pressure into the body... how much closer can one get to womb comfort?!

Use Yoga Mudras

I'm in Anuttara Raja sitting in Easy Pose. To ready us for deep breathing, Frankie tells us to do Chin Mudra by holding the thumb and forefinger together lightly with the other three remaining fingers extended.

Mudra descriptions tell us to touch fingers lightly. I intentionally touch thumb and fore finger with pressure to add more somatosensory sensation (touch and proprioception) into the finger joints. This greater pressure intensifies the pleasure and carries it up to my shoulder, enhancing body awareness. I also feel my eyes contract. Were my eyes open, this would help me focus better.

Yoga Mudras are postures of the hand that stimulate brain and body. The gestures are used mostly during meditation or in pranayama practice to direct the flow of energy through the body. This is why, when doing the Chin Mudra, I experience sensation in my eyes.

You might be skeptical and think this nonsense. In fact, there's good evidence that these different hand postures impact body and brain. Writes occupational therapist Lynn Stoller in *Sensory-Enhanced Yoga*, a technical book based on hard science for those wishing to use yoga as therapy for trauma victims: "When we position our arms, hands, and fingers in certain ways, it produces subtle shifts in posture and muscle contractions around the rib cage and other parts of the body" (p. 189). Remember we have rich nerve endings in our palms and fingers.

Add Texture

Yoga class offers several opportunities to add skin sensation through texture. You can put a soft or textured towel over the mat during floor postures, use a textured, kinesthetic mat during standing poses, and of course always practice barefoot as some beginners will try to wear socks.

Clothing

Choice of clothing adds texture. Desiring softness, my choice is an organic cotton or bamboo top and bamboo bottoms. Others, wanting a more slick texture wear mostly synthetic material, like polyester or nylon.

Mat

Choice of mat is another way to add texture. From Manduka to Gaiam Sol Drip Dry, yoga mats come in different fabrics, size, and thickness, all presenting not only a difference in practice but in different sensory experience. Some yogis prefer the traditional sticky mat, while others opt for natural rubber, cotton, hemp or jute.

For the richest mat texture, try a Gripps mat. An acupressure yoga mat, a Gripps mat incorporates ergonomically designed 'knobs' that trigger acupressure points on your hands and feet providing the full benefits of acupressure and reflexology. Gripps mats are the only NON-toxic sensory mats made of premium food-grade silicone.

Mat Cover

To get softness and better foot stability, many place a yoga mat cover on top of the mat, and especially during floor poses and Savasana. Textures range from soft to bumpy.

For exceptional softness, Kundalini yogis sit on soft lambswool, intensifying the pleasure of the practice.

Try CBD

Another way to add pleasant skin sensation is with the now popular trend in restorative yoga of adding CBD (cannabidiol) oil or cream to parts of the body.

Cannabidiol is one of 113 identified cannabinoids in cannabis plants and accounts for up to 40% of the plant's extract.

As mentioned earlier, when we are feeling good our brain naturally produces and releases the cannabinoid anandamide. Anandamide though is fragile and breaks down quickly in the body, explaining why we don't feel a perpetual state of bliss. CBD suppresses the enzyme that breaks down anandamide, creating longer lasting effects from the naturally occurring anandamide in our system. Rubbing some CBD on your skin during practice boosts yoga bliss.

ENHANCING AUDITORY SENSATION

James and Judy at Yoga South are two of the most sought-after yoga teachers in South Florida. They know their stuff and how to sequence the poses so your body flows fluidly. They vary the class to make it novel, interesting and exciting. Most of the time, they adjust you at least once during class to make you feel special.

For me, though, the most powerful draw comes equally from something of which few consciously realize: exceptionally alluring voices—James a rich, lilting tenor; Judy a commanding, hypnotic, low, contralto.

If I had to take a survey, my hunch would be that the most popular teachers are the ones who have the most captivating voices. In contrast, teachers who, expertise and command aside, have screechy, chirpy, high-pitched, flat or quiet voices, would get, at least in my observation, less attendance.

Sound matters in creating a rich yoga experience. Unpleasant voices, humming of the air conditioner, rumbling of trucks outside the window can intrude in the pleasure of your yoga class experience to a greater or less degree, depending on hearing sensitivity.

And while these unpleasantries are, for the most part outside of the studio's control, what is in control is music.

Music to Soothe the Soul

I'm lying twisted on my belly in Anuttara Raja. Tina Turner's *Sarvesham Svastir Bhavatu* with children chanting and singing in Sanskrit along with her starts to play. Ripples go through my body and a huge smile spreads across my face. I love class today even more than usual.

Music, as they say, soothes the soul. But only if the music *accords* with your sonic soul. Music that doesn't pierces nerves like a knife.

One day, I tried out a class at a new studio with a young teacher into hip hop. And hip hop it was through much of the class, composed mostly of people who could be my grandchildren. Hip hop is way too jarring for my nervous system and no way could I tolerate it for over an hour. I folded up my mat, gave her Namaste hands and left class.

Could I have just tuned it out? Not easily. Music with a strong beat stimulates the brain and speeds up the heart. Brainwaves also speed up to resonate in time with the music, alerting and charging us.

Invoking moods that vary from serenity to agitation, music choice spells the difference between an annoying, an okay, or an extraordinary class.

What kind of music is better for yoga class? It comes down to hard core neuroscience: some music revs you up and drives beta brain waves and dopamine; some music calms you and drives alpha brain waves and serotonin. For the most part, we want the latter in a yoga class, though this will vary by whether the class is largely athletic as in Vinyasa, or largely meditative, as in Anuttara Raja.

Energizing vs. Calming

Choice of music relies, first and foremost on intent: do you want the body to move with a focus on outer space, or to work toward stillness and inner space.

If you are taking yoga class for a meditative flow and stillness in poses, quiet New Age music is generally the choice as it creates slow alpha brain waves and, in meditation even slower theta brainwaves. And, indeed, after surveying 10,000 people DOYOUYOGA online found meditative music the choice 70% of the time. In this survey, *Liquid Mind* came out as the favorite.

If you are taking class with an emphasis more on athleticism than spirituality, like Power Vinyasa yoga, where the body flows quickly and vigorously through the poses and well-muscled, flexible youth abounds, *boom-boom* has advantages.

Because we process sound information below the cortex, playing music increases the heart rate and pain threshold. It greatly influences muscular and autonomic activity, making us want to move to the beat.

Grooving to the music also adds excitement and interest and serves as a depression buster. Were the teacher to play soft New Age music during this vigorous flow, the music would be asking our brains to relax when our bodies feel charged and body and brain might be fighting.

Likewise, if you play music with a beat, or arhythmic music like jazz during a meditative class the brain would be thrust out of alpha into beta, charging rather than relaxing the nervous system.

Different Strokes...

Which kind of music might you prefer in your practice? *Boom-boom* music or New Age? If, like me you are easily overstimulated, you quest calming sensation and will likely prefer slow, rhythmic beats as they encourage slow brainwaves like alpha and delta to calm down my nervous system.

If you are low arousal, *boom-boom* music is likely your choice. The beat gets your body going. The faster the beat the more it demands your focus, forcing you to stay tuned in. This is particularly appealing if you have low muscle tone, which often accompanies low arousal, as music with a beat overrides your tendency toward the lethargy that goes hand in hand with having low muscle tone.

Timing

A typical yoga class opens slowly with basic poses, moves to more challenging poses and ends in Savasana, with meditation as the purpose. Given this progression from warm-up to increasingly more intense to quiet, meditative relaxation, intuitively the music should follow suit.

Often, though it doesn't. For instance, recently class ended in Savasana with Sting's *Shape of My Heart.* Now I love this song. But when it's played during Savasana, I'm fighting to tune out the beat and words. This interferes with my mind spiraling into the cosmos.

Why might a yoga teacher play music with a beat during meditation? For one, teachers tend to choose music that will best feed *their* nervous system

If it's fast, you choose New Age; if it's slow, you choose *boom-boom* music; if easily bored by sameness, you choose jazz.

And the teacher, who must be alert throughout the class, tends to not meditate with the class.

For this reason, the teacher may lack awareness of how the beat is speeding up the nervous system. The teacher may also lack of knowledge of how words in the song stimulates left brain activity to make sense of them, throwing you out of the meditation, a right brain activity.

Of course, I'm aware that few people have my extreme sensitivity. Some people can go into the deep beyond with Jay-Z pounding. Nevertheless, consciously or not we all entrain to the sounds around us. Entrainment means body and heartbeat sync to the rhythms surrounding it. It's what makes the crowd in the stadium clap or chant in unison.

Music Choice

Let's look more closely at what music promotes the deepest relaxation during yoga practice

New Age Music

Other than during the athletic, strenuous part of Power Vinyasa yoga, New Age music tends to be the choice in yoga, as this music, by and large, is composed to create alpha and even theta brain waves, making them great stress busters.

They're also less conflicting with the teacher's voice than *boom-boom* music.

Wordless Music

Ideally, we want wordless music. When we listen to speech, Broca's area, where we process meaning, is activated. This will distract us from focusing on our body.

Human beings have a limited attention span: 120 bits per second. Listening to your instructor requires 60 bits. If the music playing has words in your native language, you're listening to two voices at once and that taxes your attention capacity. You pay less attention to what the teacher is saying if you're also being pulled away by a song. That, in turn, means less focus on sensation within the body and therefore less body awareness.

Chanting, Gongs, & Crystals

Kundalini class starts and ends with chanting. For me, it's a real draw. I get locked into a steady rhythm, almost like rocking which I often do during the chanting. Such rhythmicity encourages sensory integration of movement and sound. It does so by helping you to process heard information, employ sound recognition and reproduction and discriminate between sounds, like between B and D.

When the class chants together, oxytocin releases, creating trust. Just listening to music with others in class releases prolactin and further bonds you to fellow yogis.

For those with low muscle tone, breathing and chanting will increase stamina.

Yet, why would this be a good thing if wordless music is best? Chanting to Sanskrit, a vibrational language is different than chanting in your native language as you don't have to focus on the meaning of the words.

Vibrations

Chanting, crystals, and gongs create strong vibrations that work to internally massage and soothe your nerves.

Kundalini class generally ends with a huge, resonating gong and sometimes the hypnotic sound of crystals, making the end of class my favorite time. I purchased my own large gong for home use.

Tibetan bells or singing bowls, as well as gongs are commonly used, in Kundalini especially. They have great resonance; soothing, rich sounds and tones.

Meditation oriented classes almost always end with the class resounding in a long "om," often three oms that, with its non-melodic, long, and low sounds produced deep in your throat that produce wonderful vibration.

Drums

Drums played during the practice reach deeply into the sinews and tissues of the body. Primitive peoples used drums and chanting to induce deep meditative states. The complex polyrhythms and breathing cycles of early music can be compared to the isochronic tones of modern brain wave music.

Live Music

Some classes employ live music which creates exhilarating energy, and particularly in a packed room.

No Music

Not all yoga classes play music. Iyengar doesn't nor does Bikram yoga.

How do yogis feel about a class sans music? Most prefer music playing during yoga. In the DOYOUYOGA survey, 3 out 4 people preferred yoga with music.

As a sensory devotée, the sound of silence creates sensory deprivation. To seek sensation, I turn inward and become a victim of mind chatter, thrusting me outside my body. Feeling less pleasure, I flow through the asanas with less passion than when music is moving my body.

Iyengar doesn't play music because the class relies heavily on teacher's instruction and music would distract. I have no problem with this because the body isn't meant to flow in Iyengar: it stays steady in a pose with gaps between poses as you prop up for the next pose and listen to instruction.

In Bikram, no music is played because he thought music a distraction to concentration. This *was* a problem for me and one of the reasons I switched to Vinyasa.

Nor was Bikram correct. Rather than distracting, music enhances concentration and focus. Research confirms this: music can help you focus *more* than silence.

Movement comes from the vestibular system. The vestibular system, as you may recall, is in the inner ear and attaches to the cochlea, the part of the ear that senses sound. Like the cochlea, it is fluid-filled and lined with hair-like structures.

The system for hearing sounds evolved from the same vestibular brain network that responds to balance in space. The vestibular system still responds in some ways to sound as well as balance. Two vestibular structures, the saccule and the utricle, respond to vibrations from sounds.

This processing of sound information greatly influences muscular and autonomic activity and, subconsciously, you want to "move to the beat." *In fact,* music improves body movements. Without it, the movement system must work harder to balance. The unconscious powerful effect of music on movement has been used to help Parkinson's patients improve walking by walking with a beat.

SCENT

It's the end of the yin class at Yoga South and we lie down for Savasana. I hear my teacher Marjorie's feet coming toward me. "Hurry," I want to say, because I know what's coming.

In Savasana, Marjorie places cold washcloths on your forehead that she has infused with lavender oil. The coolness and lavender scent enhance the relaxation that much more and I want to stay there forever.

Still, scent in yoga is tricky. Each of us has different odor preferences and some people react strongly to odors. Marjorie will ask permission before placing the washcloth on your head.

Like music, if scent is right it will enhance class experience. If it's wrong, it will make your head spin and ruin the class. Some will gag from odors that repulse them. Nor can scent be tuned out as it makes a beeline from the olfactory bulb to the limbic system.

For some people almost any scent can be "wrong," including chemical free essentials oils, like lavender, which are supposed to have a rejuvenating effect on body, mind, and spirit. Though an almost universally loved essential oil, some people are bothered by the scent.

For this reason, many yoga studios are scent free and encourage people to not wear scent, especially perfume. I've had to get up numerous times and move my mat from a whiff of someone's perfume.

One scent that yoga studios use freely though is sage. Anuttara yoga has a no-scent policy as Philip reacts strongly to smell—he's so repelled by musk he's had to ask people to leave his class who are wearing it. Still, odors have such magnetic attraction, even Philip will defy his own no-scent policy and during Savasana or after class, amble around waving a sage smudge. Most smile at the pungent fragrance. One of my favorite aromas, the scent of sage heightens my joy.

If the class agrees, some studios also burn incense. A popular fragrance is Nag Champra from India, one I burn frequently at home.

I'm the canary in the coal mine when it comes to smell, not only the first to notice odors but detecting odors some never notice at all. Being surrounded by scents I like is a daily necessity. In yoga class, I violate the no-scent policy by wearing an essential oil necklace. With it around my neck, I inhale fragrant essential oils throughout class, like geranium, patchouli and lavender. It is however mild enough so that you must be quite close to me to smell it.

We've explored ways to power up sensations during practice. Now let's explore how to create a heavenly sensory yoga environment.

RECAP

ENHANCING BALANCE. Balance encompasses vestibular, proprioceptive and visual input. Yoga practice trains and improves all:

- vestibular with all the head changes;

- proprioception with all the push and pull involved in the asanas;

- visual input through focus and dristi.

WAYS TO ENHANCE BALANCE IN YOGA PRACTICE

Remove Support

Vary the Surface You Balance On

Hang Like a Bat

- Yoga inversion sling

- Yoga hanging wall

- Yoga headstand bench

Remove or Change Vision

Close Eyes. Keeping eyes closed causes you to rely on your internal sense of where you are in space to balance.

Eyes Open but Change Head Position. Look up, down, side to side or turn head.

Visualize. Visualizing the pose will help you to concentrate better and hold the pose longer.

Buy Better Mat. More expensive mats will help you balance better.

ENHANCING BODY AWARENESS

Props such as blocks or sandbags provide deeper input into joints and muscles, enhancing kinesthetic awareness of what your body's doing and fostering body awareness.

Blocks. Yoga blocks provide the stability and balance needed to encourage optimal alignment, to get you deeper into poses, and, therefore, increase strength and flexibility.

Sandbags. Weight of the sandbag anchors you down, intensifying deep pressure. With deeper pressure you realize greater awareness in the body through increased sensory input across a large surface area.

Other Helpful Props
- **Strap**

- **Balls**

- **Eye Pillow**

- **Hammock**

ENHANCING TACTILE SENSATION

Use Greater Force. Opportunities exist in several poses to push more into hands and feet and deepen pressure.

Use Wall. The wall enables you to hold, lift, or suspend a part of your body during postures; poses are deeper with greater stability and can be held longer giving you greater input into joints and muscles.

Use Ropes.

Try Partner Yoga.

Fly Through the Air. Full body deep pressure touch is ongoing during aerial yoga as your body pushes into the hammock.

Use Yoga Mudras. *Yoga Mudras* are postures of the hand that stimulate brain and body. The gestures are used mostly during meditation or in pranayama practice to direct the flow of energy through the body.

Add Texture
- **Clothing**
- **Mat**
- **Mat Cover**

ENHANCING AUDITORY SENSATION

Voice Quality. The most popular teachers are the ones who have the most captivating voices.

Choosing Music. If you are taking yoga class for a meditative flow and stillness in poses, quiet New Age music is generally the choice as it creates slow alpha brain waves and, in meditation even slower theta brainwaves. If you are taking class with an emphasis more on athleticism than spirituality, like Power Vinyasa yoga, where the body flows quickly and vigorously through the poses and well-muscled, flexible youth abounds, *boom-boom* has advantages.

Music Preference. The easily overstimulated prefer slow, rhythmic beats as they encourage slow brainwaves like alpha and delta to calm down my nervous system. Those with low arousal prefer *boom-boom* music. The beat gets your body going. The faster the beat the more it demands your focus, forcing you to stay tuned in.

Timing. A typical yoga class opens slowly with basic poses, moving to more challenging poses and ending in Savasana, with meditation as the purpose. Given this progression from warm-up to increasingly more intense to quiet, meditative relaxation, intuitively the music should follow suit.

Most Popular Music Choice. Other than during the athletic, strenuous part of Power Vinyasa yoga, New Age music tends to be the choice in yoga, as this music, by and large, is composed to create alpha and even theta brain waves, making them great stress busters.

Wordless Music. Ideally, we want wordless music. When we listen to speech, Broca's area, where we process meaning, is activated. This will distract us from focusing on our body.

Chanting. Chanting encourages sensory integration of movement and sound. When the class chants together, oxytocin releases, creating trust.

Vibrations. Chanting, crystals, and gongs create strong vibrations that work to internally massage and soothe your nerves.

No Music. Yoga classes work best with music. Music enhances concentration and focus and improves body movements. Without it, the movement system must work harder to balance.

SCENT

Each of us has different odor preferences and some people react strongly to odors. For some people almost any scent can be "wrong." For this reason, many yoga studios are scent free and encourage people to not wear scent, especially perfume.

CHAPTER 12

THE SENSORY RICH ENVIRONMENT

"The environment is the extended body. It must be peaceful."

~Deepak Chopra

Recently, I attended a yoga workshop at a yoga studio in a strip center. The walls were a pleasant light coral. In the studio two large paintings were painted on the walls, one of a meditating yogi in Easy Pose with Namaste written across it and the other of Ganesh. Yoga artifacts like a dancing Shiva were spread throughout the studio and reception room. In the center of the studio was a small table with a candle, a Buddha and some crystal bowls. The room was lit by four up-light sconces, one in each corner to give the walls a soft glow.

Sounds like an inviting place. Yet, I couldn't wait to leave.

The studio atmosphere was oppressive—a windowless enclosed small rectangle with a low eight-foot ceiling. The room could accommodate comfortably at most 20 people without feeling packed like sardines.

A slight musty smell permeated the air, likely from the sand colored carpet. That along with indoor recycled air inside the windowless room made it stultifying.

The ceiling was covered with a cream colored thick textured drape, perhaps to hide an industrial ceiling and fluorescent lights. It was nondescript and did nothing to add spark to the ceiling. I wondered how often the fabric was cleaned and if it, along with the carpet was an allergy trap.

The carpet, low ceiling, windowless small room, and oppressive air ruined the loveliness of the walls and yoga artifacts throughout. In that atmosphere, my energy and focus were spent on fighting the environment, instead of on relaxation, let alone yoga bliss.

What a switch upon entering the sacred ground of Anuttara yoga's original studio.

From the moment I stepped onto the mat in the cavernous, dark, temple-like, terra cotta brick room, with insets of Buddhas in the walls and subtle, mood enhancing up-lighting that gave the space a soft orange glow, I was hooked.

I had bought one-month of unlimited classes for $30 from Groupon and practiced Anuttara Raja for 27 of the 31 days, though the studio was a half hour ride in traffic from my home. After the class, I felt less like I had a workout than a religious experience, a rare event as I am neither religious nor spiritual.

Space matters. Sound, lighting, color, scent, temperature, texture and design, all influence mood and pleasure.

"When we are exposed to unchanging temperatures, lighting levels, noise, and sights, and when nothing around us grows or moves, our senses become dull and we function poorly."

~CAROL VENOLIA, HEALING ENVIRONMENTS

Atmosphere is central to my yoga experience. A sensory fanatic, I crave constant titillating sensation. At home, music plays almost continuously, and incense or sage wafts through the air as I sit writing at my computer or painting. Throughout the day, I dab essential oil on my skin.

My acutely sensitive eyes crave design and color. In my small, three-bedroom villa, the rooms are painted in gold, apricot, rose and teal and more than sixty of my paintings grace almost every inch of wall space.

Drab colors drain my equanimity and an empty, white wall is like death. One studio where I've practiced sports an industrial design with white everywhere: white walls in a large room; an exposed industrial white ceiling of white structural grids that, in the dim room appears as a variation of dull gray. Luckily the lights are kept dim and, eyes closed throughout the practice I shut out the dull atmosphere.

Am I the exception? Are others more laissez-faire about environment? Yes, of course. Nevertheless, people will behave differently if the lights are too bright or too dim, the music too loud or too soft, the room too small and people too close, or too large and people spread too far apart creating a sense of isolation.

The nervous system registers and reacts to external stimuli, whether one is conscious of the sensation or not. One study found that very low-level sounds (30 to 50 decibels), like a flushing toilet down the hall, cause people to shift from deep sleep to light sleep. Another study found that people working in a noisy environment showed increased levels of the stress hormone epinephrine, even if they didn't feel particularly stressed. While another study found that people working in a room permeated by the odor of burnt dust lost their appetites, even though they didn't notice the smell.

Of course, everyone has unique sensory preferences. Still, some consensus exists of what an ideal yoga studio is like and most share common features: a Zen-like feel; softly painted walls; yoga artifacts throughout; a wooden floor; windows in the studio; a high ceiling.

Yoga South is an example. With its soft apricot walls, insets of yogi images like Shiva, and other charming touches to greet you the atmosphere exudes a spiritual feeling, enhancing tranquility and quietude and radiating positive energy.

The large studio has wooden floors, a high ceiling to create plenty of oxygen-filled airy spaces, a calming color scheme of soft, pale gold, and windows to create brightness and boost mental health.

Let's look more closely at common design elements in a yoga studio.

VISUAL

Color

Color is not just a visual experience in a yoga studio. Color sets the tone, impacting mood and emotion.

Ideally, studios should be painted in warm, subdued colors like peach or gold. Mildly energizing, inviting and positive, these warm colors brighten up a space without overwhelming the eye and create an expansive and uplifting feel.

Using such a warm subdued color also offsets the bright stimulating colors of yoga mats and apparel. In an athletic oriented class, the contrast helps make the class what it's designed to be: at once energizing and calming.

In a studio more focused with a meditative practice, walls might be painted with "cool" colors like blues, greens, and purples. These colors foster inward orientation and provide calm and comfort.

To be avoided in any yoga class are calm but too-cool white or gray walls as these colors can under-stimulate and even invite depression for those prone to the blues.

Eyestrain

Also, of consideration in choosing wall color is the effect on the eyes. In athletic oriented classes like Power Vinyasa yoga, where eyes are kept mostly open throughout the practice, bright colors in the studio like orange could produce eye fatigue. A cool color like blue in contrast would tire the eyes because reflected or direct blue light makes focusing difficult. While too much white could cause glare and constrict the pupils.

Creating Space & Warmth

If you wish to make a studio appear larger, choose light colors for the walls. Light colored walls reflect more light and create the illusion of space, making a smaller room look larger and a darker room brighter, while dark colors narrow space.

Rich, vibrant colors, like yellow, will make a large room feel more intimate, while greens and blues create large, cool airy spaces.

Color also influences temperature. A blue room feels cooler than a warm-colored or neutral room at the same temperature, while highlights of reds, oranges, or yellows will make a dim, cool room noticeably warmer.

Emotional Impact

Do most people sense the effect of color on their being? Yes, although it may be felt unconsciously.

Color effects come from an energy that goes beyond sight. Many blind people can differentiate colors by pressing fingers or hands over an object and feeling color vibrations: some colors feel hot; some feel cool. Sighted subjects wearing blindfolds respond differently to different colors as well.

Most people's mood shifts according to the colors that surround them. Before going on stage or TV, performers and speakers wait in the "green room," as green has a restful effect. Schoolrooms painted blue settle hyperactive children, though choosing the correct color blue is tricky as darker shades of blue link to sadness.

Pink is thought to have a calming effect. One shade known as "drunk-tank pink" has been used in prisons to calm inmates. Sports teams sometimes paint the opposing team's locker room pink to keep the players passive and less energetic.

WALLS

As you enter Yoga South, a large Ganesh painted on the wall diagonal to the reception desk greets you.

On a wall in the hallway is a meditative painting I created and gifted to the studio (painted in orange, amber and yellow burnt sienna hues).

Inside the studio, a small Buddha sits against the wall on the large shelf housing props and cubbies for personals. Painted on the forward facing wall are star like shapes at eye level for dristi. The walls themselves are bare as they are used as a prop for inversions and wall work.

Paintings, inserts, artifacts on shelves and so on add ambience and interest to a yoga studio. Images inside the studio though can be distracting and walls are generally kept sparse, particularly in studios that use the wall as props or have props like straps on the wall. The exception is images placed high on the wall. One studio where I've practiced has a huge sign high up in the front of the room that says, "Breathe." I love it as it works wonderfully to remind me to pay attention to breath.

To Mirror or not Mirror

Mirrors cover three walls at Anuttara yoga. I take advantage and during Anuttara Raja place my mat in the corner so I can see myself in front and to the side. Because of my spinal issues, my body is crooked while sitting in Easy Pose and I'm leaning to the right. The mirrors act as visual/spatial aid to help me to check my alignment and correct my position, and I re-align my body so it's straight. Without seeing myself in the mirror, I would remain leaning to the right.

Having mirrored walls helps people like me who have crooked spines, as well the hypermobile to ensure they are not hyperextending.

There are other advantages. By adding a wall of mirrors on the front wall, you create the illusion of much more space. As part of his brand, Bikram designed his studios with mirrored walls.

But there are disadvantages. Mirroring a wall eliminates the use of that wall as a prop to enhance input into the joints and muscles and increase proprioception. You won't find mirrors on the walls of an Iyengar class.

Mirrored walls also interfere with body sensing. To enhance body awareness, ideally you want to experience the messages coming from within your body, not from viewing yourself in a mirror. The more you practice without a mirror, the more you feed your proprioceptive sense. Sensing what your body is doing and where it is in space helps to discover what you can do, in that moment, and to avoid going beyond what your body is ready to do.

Another problem occurs if mirrors cover more than the front wall as you might not be able to look away from your body. If you have a negative body image, as many people do who are overweight or who have low muscle tone, seeing your body in the mirror will create discomfort.

LIGHTING

Lighting can change the mood of a studio considerably.

Natural light with muted sunlight works best. Yoga studios exposed to much natural light change both ambience *and* feeling according to whether the day is sunny and light or raining and grayish—all evoking a different mood. Enclosed studios that use artificial light evoke the same mood day in and day out, regardless of weather, making the atmosphere less interesting.

To create a relaxing, Zen-like atmosphere, a slightly dim environment works best in a yoga studio. A caveat though.

Lighting should not be too dim as the student should be able to clearly see the room, as balance relies on vision.

If a studio lacks enough windows to permit natural light and you must use artificial light, some general rules apply.

Avoid Bright Spots

One studio where I've practiced has four round metal patterned cylinders hanging from the ceiling. They give the studio charm and make for interesting lighting as the light penetrates through the design on the metal.

Unfortunately though, a naked light bulb hangs in the center. During practice, yogis turn their face in all directions, including upwards. Having a light right above the head is not only visually disturbing but can also interrupt focus and concentration. A light above your head is especially disconcerting during floor time in the last half hour of class when, if you're anywhere near the hanging light and your eyes are open the light points directly into your eyes.

The experts tell us to avoid not only bright spots but dark spots by spreading lighting through the space. Pot (recessed) lights, track lighting or up-light wall sconces work best to avoid light shining directly into the eyes. If you have mirrors, avoid light bouncing off mirrors.

Choose Lightbulbs Carefully

Yoga is taught everywhere from gyms to offices. And that means often you get overhead compact fluorescent lightbulb (CFLs)—my worst nightmare. Five minutes under CRL's and I'm jittery, fragmented, irritable and too drained to think, let alone exert a huge muscular effort in yoga.

Though they bother me more than most people, CFLs directly affect the nervous system in all people.

Fluorescent lights create stress. They reduce heart rate variability (vagal tone), raise blood pressure and cortisol level, lower body temperature during sleep, and reduce deep Delta, the deepest sleep.

They're also noisy and they buzz, making them especially unpleasant in the yoga studio where distractions should be avoided.

And they flicker. In sensitive people, this produces headaches, as well as tics, and seizures in those with epilepsy. My eyes are profoundly disturbed by the flicker and I flee immediately to the farthest corner, astonished at the people in my class who don't! Even more astonishing to me is how some people don't even notice the flicker.

Due to improved lighting technology, visible flicker has diminished, and, because fluctuations happen so rapidly, is now largely invisible to the eye. Yet the brain picks up what the eye can't see and, whether conscious of it or not the light irritates the nervous system, evoking the flight/fight response. In response to bright light, the pupil of the eye should contract. But with the extremely rapid dimming and brightening of high-frequency flicker, the pupils could remain dilated.

A 2010 study found that people in an office setting with non-visible flicker from conventional fluorescent lights had heightened central nervous system arousal and lower performance accuracy.

Ultraviolet Light

Fluorescent lights also emit a bright ultraviolet light that, in relatively high amounts cause sleep disturbance as a result of melatonin suppression. The high color (colder/bluer) temperature of fluorescent light stimulates the non-visual pathways from the eye to various parts of the brain that involve the body clock and arousal levels, stress hormones, emotions, and muscle tension.

What Light Is Best?

The healthiest light is sunlight or candlelight, followed by incandescent though those have been mostly phased out, then halogen, then LEDs, then CFLs.

For the purest artificial light, use full-spectrum lighting like Ott lights, which are pure white. Sunlight though is your best bet to get the Zenned-out vibes you're looking for in a yoga studio.

Most studios where I practice have a dimmer on their light switches to dim or brighten the lights depending on the class. When doing difficult asanas you need brighter lighting both to get the heart rate up and to facilitate balance. Remember, balance is composed of three components: vestibular, proprioceptive and visual. A dim room makes balancing more challenging. When doing relaxation or breathing exercises, dim lights create the right atmosphere. During Savasana, lights are off.

Colored Lights

To create atmosphere, try colored lights in different colors. Some of the best color lights that will enhance your yoga classes are:

Green

Green lights give off safe and soothing vibes that help you practice yoga with greater ease.

Blue

For morning classes, blue light will create calm and peace, while at the same time making you more fully alert.

Red

The light frequency of red color is highly stimulating. Practicing yoga in red lights help boost blood circulation, improve metabolism, and elevate your energy levels.

Violet

During meditation, violet lights will encourage inner peace and mental calm.

WINDOWS

The first time I walked into the yoga studio at Casa Mannabliss in Delray Beach, Florida, I knew I was going to love class.

The studio is in a restored old, vintage home near downtown Delay Beach, giving it, obviously, a homey feeling. Restoring homes and converting them for restaurants and businesses is a common practice in downtown Delray Beach, which has been designated an historic district, and gives the town an old, country charm. Many Delray homes were built in the 1930's.

Formerly the living/dining room of the home, the studio itself has long windows on three sides, covered by transparent white drapes, a high, small rectangular window on one wall covered with a wooden lattice, and a glass door on the fourth side. Though on the small side, comfortably accommodating perhaps 30 people all the light in the studio makes the room feel large and expansive.

Windows in a yoga studio offer light, fresh air, aesthetics and a natural feeling. If you have a window or door with a view to the outside, psychologically seeing the edge of the horizon anchors and grounds us. A windowless studio, in contrast has a boxed in, artificial feeling.

CEILING

Ceiling Height

One of the highlights of traveling in Europe is visiting ancient cathedrals with their vaulted ceilings, arches and stained-glass windows. Knowing the appeal of such expansive space, architects and builders in South Florida often replicate the old architecture with elegant and luxurious high volume and vaulted ceilings, and rooms divided with tall arches. They give them names like Villa Valencia, Saint Tropez.

Entry level housing in contrast invariably has a standard 8-foot ceiling as do many yoga classes held in industrial or strip centers. This traditional height can look cramped in a large room and contract the studio space. And, while the height may be sufficient to accommodate a 6' 4" person with arms extended straight above their head, it's far more comfortable and inviting for yogis to stretch their arms and feet in an upward position with a taller ceiling.

According to design experts, the best ceiling height is 10 feet or higher. Interesting and aesthetically appealing, higher ceilings exude an immediate sense of space, air, and light. In a yoga studio, higher ceilings impart a cathedral-like, almost spiritual setting.

It's no accident that the studios that have held my attendance the longest, like Yoga South and Anuttara have high ceilings.

High ceilings trigger tendencies toward visuospatial exploration and prompt us to think more freely. This induces creativity and positive feelings, a mindset associated with long-term yoga practice. Lower ceilings in contrast lead to more confined thinking.

This appeal is backed by research. In a 2015 neuroscience study led by Oshin Vartanian, subjects, while in a brain scanner, looked at 200 images of rooms. Half of the pictures showed rooms with high ceilings, half with low. Participants were asked to indicate whether they considered the room "beautiful" or "not beautiful." Rooms with higher ceilings were more likely to be judged beautiful.

The researchers found heightened activity related to high ceilings in the left precuneus and left middle frontal gyrus—two areas associated with visuospatial exploration. This supports the notion that high ceilings capture attention and engage desire to observe our surroundings.

Enclosed rooms activated the anterior midcingulate cortex, the region of the brain that receives messages from the amygdala. The authors suggest this reduced visual perception and locomotion, characteristic of enclosed spaces. Emotionally, this instilled the desire to leave a space rather than stay. My sentiment exactly.

Vaulted Ceilings

Vaulted ceilings give a majestic, temple like feeling to a space. In a yoga studio, they add a light and airy feeling. A vaulted ceiling with natural wood color slats gives Casa MannaBliss great energy and adds to my enjoyment of the yoga class.

Ceiling Embellishment

High volume ceilings of at least 20 feet high added to the temple like feeling of the cavernous Anuttara yoga studio. To fill in the space and add interest, silk-like fabric drapes of varying colors billowed across the ceiling. During an Anuttara Raja class especially this worked well as many poses were done prone. Looking up at the colorful, silky ceiling added to the pleasure of the pose and took your mind off the torture of lying twisted like a pretzel for five minutes, every fiber in you screaming for release.

Angles & Curves

Angles add interest and freshness and we know how the brain grooves to novelty. Recently neuroscientists have shown that this affection for curves isn't just a matter of personal taste; it's hard-wired into the brain.

Roundness seems to be a universal human pleasure. Time and again, when people are asked to choose between an object that's linear and one that's curved, they prefer the latter. This is true of both men and women.

In one recent study researchers reported that test participants were far more likely to consider a room beautiful when it was flush with curves rather than full of straight lines. Using FMRI scans to peer into subjects' brains when they viewed a curved design, researchers discovered more activity in a brain area called the anterior cingulate cortex, an area of the brain involved in emotion.

Of course, unless you design your own yoga space, curved walls are unlikely. But you can bring in curves in other ways. At Yoga South, there's a curved inset in the wall with a statue of Shiva. At Anuttara Yoga, the reception area has a curved couch wrapped around two sides of the room.

Adding wall features like an oval mirror or round image painted on the wall, or adding a curved panel above a window to give the illusion that it is arched, are easy ways to add appealing curves to the studio.

TACTILE

FLOORING

Floors at yoga studios run from wood to rubber to carpet. At Yoga South, the floor is covered with a beige wood, as is the floor at Casa Mannabliss. This floor makes it easy to balance and soft to tread on. At Anuttara yoga, the floor is covered with black rubber. The owner believes rubber carries earth's frequencies and connects us more to the earth than would a wooden floor.

What's best and why?

The general consensus for a yoga studio floor is hardwood, cork or bamboo flooring. This type of flooring is contaminant-resistance and shock-absorbent as well. And these materials elevate the overall beauty of the space.

While hardwood is the most popular, bamboo flooring has some advantage over hardwood as it is durable, flexible, soft under foot (or head or hand or stomach depending on the pose) and it withstands heat, moisture and humidity better than hardwood. Cork, however, is soft and durable and comfortable against the body.

Avoid tile, vinyl, and concrete floors as they are cold and hard. And avoid carpets.

Carpet Studio Woes

My first Bikram classes were practiced at an athletic club. Though Bikram studios are supposed to have a carpeted floor, as Bikram felt carpeting more forgiving to joints than hard floors this room had a wooden floor as the studio was not designed specifically for Bikram yoga classes.

After not practicing Bikram for several years, I decided to give Bikram another shot, when I moved to Delray Beach as a Bikram studio was close by.

The minute I walked into the studio, I almost swooned from the vinegar-like odor emanating from the carpet. That and the musty odor from lack of fresh air, to say nothing of the humid high heat, made me feel as if I needed a mask.

Carpets are a bad idea in a yoga studio. Carpets get filthy and stink. They smell. Nor can they be cleaned often enough to remove all the dirt and bacteria that accumulate, making it an allergy sufferer's nightmare. According to Google, the average amount of bacteria found in a homeowner's carpet is 200,000 organisms per square inch—and Florida is the allergy capital.

In a yoga studio, carpets are not only full of bacteria but can be dangerous. Hot yoga studios are responsible for fires, roof collapses, and code infringements. A studio owner was evicted in Florida because the foul odors were detectable from blocks away. Inside, it was "an infectious petri dish of mold, fungi and Legionnaire's Disease", according to the IAQ expert who was called in.

TEMPERATURE

People think I'm fussy, and I am. Though I no longer jump out of my skin at noise, light touch, or sunlight, I'm bothered more than most by "ordinary" sensation.

To help people to understand my irritability, I ask them to imagine the discomfort of feeling uncomfortably hot. In South Florida where I live, people would give up eye teeth before giving up air conditioning.

Everyone has a different optimum temperature level. I love heat and gravitate toward yoga classes where I sweat. In the past 30 years since I've been living in Florida, I've used my air conditioning a handful of times.

Others get totally discombobulated from heat. Women in menopause flee hot yoga classes and seek yoga classes with air-conditioning. Some dislike heated classes because the sensation of sweat on their skin annoys them. They'll sit under a fan or near an open window or door in the studio and retreat to the shower immediately following class.

These preferences can't be easily overcome. Temperature matters for comfort. If overly hot or cold, it's hard to focus on anything else. The most aesthetically pleasing yoga studio will become debilitating if the temperature feels too warm or too cold, too dry or too stuffy.

Air quality matters also. I dislike being closed inside without fresh air and abhor the indoor, recycled air created by heating and air conditioning at some studios. Too cold in the summer and too hot and dry in the winter, artificial air control makes me drowsy, sluggish and irritable. How lucky I am to live in Florida where windows and doors can be kept open most of the year to allow fresh air inside the yoga studio.

Other people seem less aware of the discomfort and have less of a problem with a heated or air-conditioned yoga class.

Hot Yoga

Still, given that most dislike heat, how does one explain the popularity of hot yoga? In hot yoga, temperature ranges from 90 degrees F to 108 degrees F with varying levels of humidity the room.

Bikram yoga is the supreme hot yoga. Creating what Bikram calls the "torture chambers," the room must be heated to 105 degrees with 40 percent humidity. The class feels like being in a Norwegian sweat lodge and you drip, drenching yoga clothes in perspiration. At the end of class, you can wring them out.

Granted, there's good reason why the room is overheated. Muscles warm quickly and stretch with little trouble. This gets you into postures more easily and helps prevent injuries. Working up a good sweat also eliminates waste products through your skin.

Still, few people love heat. Why does hot yoga attract so many? One answer is the release of oxytocin. Researchers have found that hot environments, warm temperatures and increased sweating activate specific oxytocin-producing parts of the brain. Sweating gets us feeling loved, loving, and connected.

RECAP

Ideal Yoga Studios: a Zen-like feel; softly painted walls; yoga artifacts throughout; a wooden floor; windows in the studio; a high ceiling.

VISUAL

COLOR. Color sets the tone of a yoga studio, impacting mood and emotion. Ideally, studios should be painted in warm, subdued colors like peach or gold. To be avoided are calm but too-cool white or gray walls as these colors can under-stimulate and even invite depression for those prone to the blues.

Eyestrain. When eyes are kept mostly open throughout the practice, bright colors in the studio like orange could produce eye fatigue, while a cool color like blue would tire the eyes because reflected or direct blue light makes focusing difficult. Too much white could cause glare and constrict the pupils.

Creating Space & Warmth. Light colors for the walls make a studio look larger and create the illusion of space. Rich, vibrant colors, like yellow, will make a large room feel more intimate, while greens and blues create large, cool airy spaces.

Emotional Impact.
- Green has a restful effect.

- Blue settles hyperactive children.

- Pink is thought to have a calming effect.

WALLS. ~~Paintings, inserts, artifacts~~ on shelves and so on add ambience and interest to a yoga studio. Images inside the studio though can be distracting and walls are generally kept sparse, particularly in studios that use the wall as props or have props like straps on the wall. The exception is images placed high on the wall.

To Mirror or Not Mirror. Mirrors act as visual/spatial aid to help check my alignment and correct position. But there are disadvantages.

- Mirroring a wall eliminates the use of that wall as a prop to enhance input into the joints and muscles and increase proprioception;

- They interfere with body sensing.

LIGHTING

Lighting can change the mood of a studio considerably. Natural light with muted sunlight works best.

Avoid Bright Spots. Having a light right above the head is visually disturbing and can also interrupt focus and concentration.

Avoid Fluorescent Lights

- Fluorescent lights create stress.

- They reduce heart rate variability (vagal tone).

- They raise blood pressure and cortisol level.

- They lower body temperature during sleep, and reduce deep Delta, the deepest sleep.

- They're noisy and buzz.

- They flicker.

What Light Is Best? The healthiest light is sunlight or candlelight, followed by incandescent though those are being phased out, then halogen, then LEDs, then CFLs. For the purest artificial light, use full-spectrum lighting like Ott lights to get the Zenned-out vibes you're looking for in a yoga studio.

Colored Lights. To create atmosphere, try colored lights in different colors. Some of the best color lights that will enhance your yoga classes are:

Green. Give off safe and soothing vibes that help you practice yoga with greater ease.

Blue. Creates calm and peace, while at the same time making you more fully alert.

Red. Boosts blood circulation, improves metabolism, and elevates energy levels.

Violet. During meditation, violet lights will encourage inner peace and mental calm.

Windows in a yoga studio offer light, fresh air, aesthetics and a natural feeling.

CEILING

Ceiling Height. According to design experts, the best ceiling height is 10 feet or higher. Interesting and aesthetically appealing, higher ceilings exude an immediate sense of space, air, and light. In a yoga studio, higher ceilings impart a cathedral-like, almost spiritual setting.

Vaulted Ceilings. Vaulted ceilings give a majestic, temple like feeling to a space. In a yoga studio, they add a light and airy feeling.

Angles & Curves. Angles add interest and freshness. Add wall features like an oval mirror or round image painted on the wall, or add a curved panel above a window to give the illusion that it is arched.

TACTILE

FLOORING. The general consensus for a yoga studio floor is hardwood, cork or bamboo flooring. This type of flooring is contaminant-resistance and shock-absorbent as well. And these materials elevate the overall beauty of the space. Avoid tile, vinyl, and concrete as they are cold and hard. Especially avoid carpets in a yoga studio.

Carpet Studio Woes. Carpets are a bad idea in a yoga studio. Carpets get filthy and stink. They smell. Nor can they be cleaned often enough to remove all the dirt and bacteria that accumulate, making it an allergy sufferer's nightmare.

TEMPERATURE. Temperature matters for comfort. If overly hot or cold, it's hard to focus on anything else.

Hot Yoga. In hot yoga, temperature ranges from 90 degrees F to 108 degrees F with varying levels of humidity the room. High heat and humidity stresses many. They also have advantages.

- Hot environments, warm temperatures and increased sweating activate specific oxytocin-producing parts of the brain.

- Sweating gets us feeling loved, loving, and connected.

PUTTING IT ALTOGETHER

We're at the end of our journey. I hope this book has strengthened, affirmed or perhaps introduced yoga as the smoothest, clearest, straightest path you could choose to traverse in life.

Twists and turns. Wrong turns and unknown paths. We all encounter them daily. Yoga sets our path forward and upward to scale mountains. Mountains of fear. Mountains of uncertainty. Mountains of aches and pains. Grounding us, stabilizing us, comforting us, sharpening us, it gives us the vision to see beyond the clouds and into the clearing.

In this lazy, hardly-treading-a-foot world, it is savior. Without movement to feed our vestibular, proprioceptive and tactile systems sufficiently to give us womb comforts and greater neurological integrity, we'd all fall into the pit. Yoga offers a way out of our biologically unnatural and destructive modern lifestyle of no steps and missteps, of being ungrounded and out of touch with earth and self.

For super yogis I hope the journey reaffirms what you've known all along. That yoga takes many of the bumps out of the road and smooths out body and mind with a steady pace and controlled steps. For yoga teachers, I hope this journey will give you more ways to smooth out the missteps of your students.

For those taking first steps onto a mat, or considering it, I hope you will see yoga as the path to take—the path to a better body, the way to a clearer mind, the trail to more uplifting mood, the route to more stable emotions.

For me yoga has averted not just a bumpy ride but a treacherous one. One that took me down a steep hill into an abyss with deep terrifying crevices at every turn. My path, now, is not smooth. It never will be. But it's far less bumpy, far less crooked, far less an incline than it would have been without having stepped onto the mat for the last twenty-five years and, I hope at least twenty more.

SUGGESTED READING

Claire Dederer, *Poser, my life in twenty-three yoga poses* (NY: Farrar, Straus & Giroux, 2011).

Louise Goldberg, *Yoga Therapy for Children with Autism and Special Needs* (NY: W.W. Norton, 2013).

Sharon Heller, *Too Loud, Too Bright, Too Fast, Too Tight: What to do if you are sensory defensive in an overstimulating world* (NY: HarperCollins, December, 2002).

Sharon Heller, *Uptight & Off Center, How Sensory Processing Disorder Throws Adults off Baance & How to Create Stability* (Symmetry, 2015).

Patt Lind-Kyle, *Heal Your Mind Rewire Your Brain* (Energy Psychology Press, 2010).

Scott McCredie, *Balance, In Search of the Lost Sense* (NY: Little, Brown & Co., 2017).

John Ratey, *Spark, The Revolutionary New Science of Exercise and the Brain* (NY: Little, Brown, 2013).

Rachel S. Scheider, *Making Sense* (Sensory World, 2016).

_____ Lynn Stoller, *Sensory Enhanced Yoga for Self-Regulation and Trauma Healing* (Handspring, 2019).

About the Author

Sharon Heller, PhD is an author, developmental psychologist, consultant for sensory processing disorder, and yogi. She lives in a villa in Delray Beach, FL. with two fabulous felines and paintings of her art covering every inch of wall (nom de artiste "Anya.")

Made in the USA
Las Vegas, NV
12 November 2021

34250625R00187